The Gold
Museum

Banco de la República

Bogotá   Colombia

W9-ATP-509

GALLERY 1

The Working of Metals 15

GALLERY 2

People and Gold in Pre-Hispanic Colombia 31

Pendant
3.4 X 3.5 CM
CARIBBEAN PLAINS,
ZENÚ TRADITION
200 B.C. - 1600 A.D.
O06450

Pendant
7.1 X 3.2 CM
RESTREPO,
VALLE DEL CAUCA
CALIMA REGION,
YOTOCO PERIOD
200 B.C. - 1300 A.D.
O06700

Introduction

The Banco de la República Gold Museum not only preserves and investigates one of the most important collections of pre-Hispanic metallurgy in the world, it also makes that collection widely known and exhibits it. As its history has unfolded, so this institution has become a symbol of Colombia's cultural memory. The collection dates back to 1939, when Banco de la República, the central bank of Colombia, acquired an object of outstanding beauty, a Quimbaya lime container, or poporo. Nurtured by clearly differentiated scientific, museographic, architectural and aesthetic approaches, the collection has been displayed in four places, each of which has reflected the spirit and intentions of the age. The first exhibition was in the 1940s, perhaps of the entire collection, in the Banco de la República Boardroom. In 1947, the collection was put on permanent display in a room that was opened to special visitors, and then from 1959, the general public were able to admire it, when a basement in the Bank's office building was specially adapted for the purpose. The Museum as such dates back to 1968, when a building was erected that had been conceived and designed as a modern museum, with all the necessary trappings and equipment, not to mention its own staff of archaeologists, architects, museographers and teachers.

The future needs and requirements of the Museum and its collection were analysed in 1998. The needs that were identified included the possibility of permanently exhibiting a larger number of objects, and renewing the scientific approach, while in the field of museography, it was proposed that the museographic systems should be updated by introducing new technologies in showcases, lighting, and special devices so that the Museum could move into the 21st century. It was also deemed necessary to provide the Museum with areas that would enable it to put on a more varied programme, and to improve the services that visitors look for nowadays in museums.

The result is the 21st century Gold Museum that this visitor's guide describes. The scientific and museographic setting for both the exhibition and this publication means that a new version can be offered of the ancient metallurgy cycle in Colombia: gold is mined or extracted, it is worked, it is used, it is symbolised, and then it is offered up so it can return once more to the earth. It is thus a scientific and curatorial approach, one which encourages and suggests diverse ways of looking at the collection in the four permanent exhibition galleries: The Working of Metals, People and Gold in pre-Hispanic Colombia, Cosmology and Symbolism, and The Offering. For visitors who wish to study the collection in greater depth, thematic visits are offered, together with pedagogical animations, audio guides in Spanish, English and French, and a multimedia room where visitors can study and do research.

The Gold Museum is thus a place where Colombia's pre-Hispanic past and memory come alive and can be viewed in an exceptional manner. But it also propounds and fosters cultural diversity today. The Exploratorium, which has been conceived as somewhere that will arouse curiosity and raise questions, is a wonderful place for children, youngsters, even adults, to go beyond merely acquiring knowledge, and to ask questions about who we are, what languages the indigenous and Afro-Colombian societies who live in our country speak, what archaeological heritage is, and many more, so that this experience can make them want to tour the rest of the Museum and view it through the eyes of a curious researcher.

The Museum is also a research centre, a venue for academic interaction, dissemination and cooperation, and a place where national and international strategic alliances are forged. It boasts a temporary exhibitions gallery, an auditorium, and study rooms. In short, its transformation has enabled it to become a cultural centre whose essence, raison d'être and justification are to be found, of course, in the exhibitions and in the programmes it arranges, but it is also a place where visitors can enjoy themselves. This guide, which is arranged in the same order as the Museum itself, has been produced by the curators, and looks in depth at the subjects and the collections displayed. It will allow you to find out more about the Museum and its collections before your visit. When you are inside the Museum, it will guide you around. And after you have left, it will act as a souvenir, tempting you to return, not just once but many times. **CIB**

Floor Plan

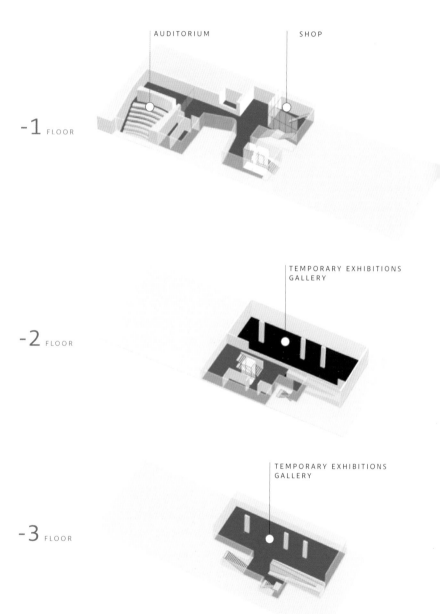

AUDITORIUM

SHOP

-1 FLOOR

TEMPORARY EXHIBITIONS GALLERY

-2 FLOOR

TEMPORARY EXHIBITIONS GALLERY

-3 FLOOR

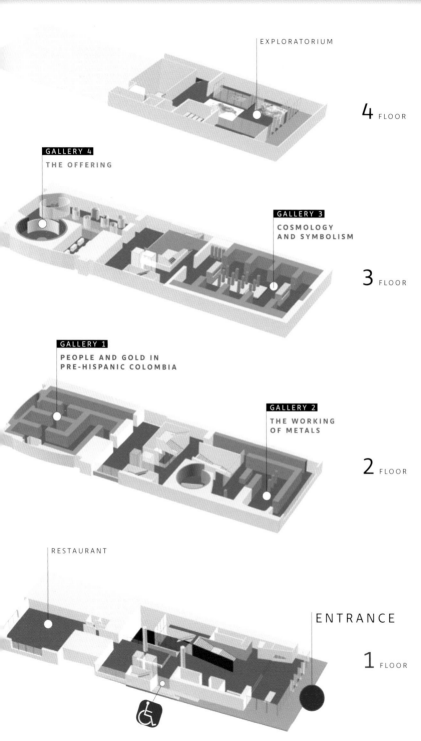

EXPLORATORIUM

4 FLOOR

GALLERY 4
THE OFFERING

GALLERY 3
COSMOLOGY
AND SYMBOLISM

3 FLOOR

GALLERY 1
PEOPLE AND GOLD IN
PRE-HISPANIC COLOMBIA

GALLERY 2
THE WORKING
OF METALS

2 FLOOR

RESTAURANT

ENTRANCE

1 FLOOR

The New Gold Museum

Mankind lived for thousands of years without metals, but when they were discovered and used, a giant leap occurred in technological and social development. From then on, peoples who knew how to work metals created a special relationship with them. The Gold Museum develops this idea, as far as the inhabitants of pre-Hispanic Colombia were concerned, in four exhibition galleries. A video at the entrance to the first gallery reflects on the role that metals play in life today, and takes the visitor on a journey into the past to reveal, through a historical account, how our ancestors discovered and worked metals.

The first gallery describes the mining, manufacturing and finishing processes that enabled metal objects to be produced in pre-Hispanic Colombia. The visitor becomes immersed in the world of transforming gold, copper, silver and platinum, materials from which the ancient metalsmiths made thousands of different objects. Finished metal objects adorned man, and in doing so, they transformed him. And as tools, they opened up new possibilities. The second gallery looks more closely at the use and context of metals in pre-Hispanic Colombian societies.

Metal transcends its material object status. Ornaments can encode and express American mythology and symbology. The third gallery explores the way in which the great mythical themes, shamanism and symbolism, were expressed in metal objects, with emphasis on their aesthetic conception, which makes them important works of universal art. The cycle is closed when the metals return to the earth. These materials, which have been transformed and imbued with profound meanings, return to their place of origin in the form of offerings. The fourth gallery immerses the visitor, who has been exploring, in the Muisca raft, the pre-Hispanic portrayal of a sacred ritual, in the fascinating world of offering ceremonies, which were epitomised by Guatavita Lake. This sensory experience completes the exhibition. **RLL**

Anthropomorphous vessel
13.6 X 10.8 CM
RESTREPO, VALLE DEL CAUCA
CALIMA, ILAMA PERIOD
1600 B.C. - 100 A.D.
C04530

In the beginning was the sea, everything was dark.
There was no sun, no moon, there were no people,
no animals, no plants. The sea was the Mother; the
Mother was not a person or thing, the Mother was
nothing at all. She was the spirit of what was to come,
she was memory and thought.

KOGUI MYTHOLOGY

11

Ika Indians
PHOTO: GERARDO
REICHEL-DOLMATOFF.
BIBLIOTECA LUIS ÁNGEL
ARANGO DEL BANCO
DE LA REPÚBLICA.

The Working of Metals

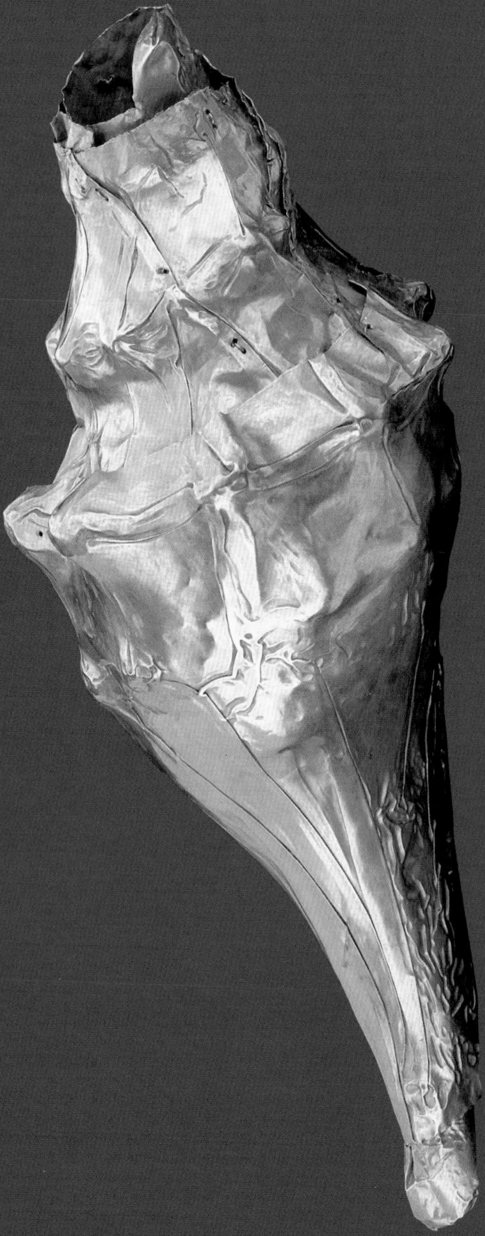

Snail Cover
14.80 X 30 CM
RESTREPO, VALLE DEL CAUCA
CALIMA REGION, YOTOCO PERIOD
200 B.C. - 1300 A.D.
O03316

*T*HE HISTORY of metals can be traced back nine thousand years, to the Near East. The first metal used, in Palestine and Anatolia, was native copper. During the following centuries, man learned to extract copper from minerals and to mix it with tin to make bronze. Strong tools were used in agriculture and for making handicrafts, and production grew. Gold and silver adorned important dignitaries, and were buried alongside them in their graves.

New technical processes made it possible to work other metals. Bronze and iron metallurgy thus developed hand in hand, together with metalwork using gold and silver. Virtually all peoples in the Old World had metals by 1000 B.C.

By the time of the fall of the Roman Empire, metal implements were part of everyday life. Trade was unthinkable without coins, as were everyday activities without metal tools. The religions of the ancient world turned to gold and silver for manufacturing sacred objects. States in Western Africa used bronze to decorate royal citadels from 1300 onwards. Convoys crossed the desert to provide the blacksmiths with raw materials and to distribute their products.

The ancient inhabitants of South America began to work copper and gold around 1500 B.C. By 500 A.D., metallurgy was already a common activity from central Mexico right down to northern Chile and Argentina. Each region developed its own styles.

In pre-Hispanic Colombia, metallurgy was primarily goldwork. Many different styles were created over a period of two thousand years, and thousands of objects were made. The European Conquest in 1500 cut this development short and caused metalwork production to disappear. Tremendous progress has been made in metal production in the last three hundred years. The vast industry uses millions of tons of metal. The history of mankind in the last nine thousand years is the history of metals, for it is with them that we have built the world we live in. RLL

Gold mining

Metallurgy in Colombia

Miners and Metalsmiths

When a miner makes tunnels or aqueducts, or diverts watercourses, he intervenes in nature and triggers off a transformation process. In ancient times, these specialists were respected and held in high esteem, because they knew the secrets of the earth and ways to extract metals.

Metals are found in nature in the form of compounds, minerals mixed with other elements. These are known as ores, while the places where they are found are called deposits. There are primary deposits, in the form of seams in the mountains, and secondary ones, where a mountain has eroded and the metal is released, generally in torrents and on the beds of rivers and streams. Before a metal can be worked, a metallurgist has to subject it to processes that will clean it and remove the accompanying oxides and minerals: this is known as smelting metals.

Just as they are today in many traditional societies, the metallurgist and metalworker must have been viewed as special, important members of the community in the past. They possessed the skill to convert a rock into a shiny metal, and could make it rigid or flexible. In the territory that is now known as Colombia, the metalworkers' knowledge - about the physical and chemical properties and characteristics of metals and their skill in working them - manifested itself in a great variety of alloys, techniques and forms, which bear testimony to their particular way of viewing the world. **JSS**

Crown
5.5 X 47.5 CM
RESTREPO, VALLE DEL CAUCA
CALIMA REGION, YOTOCO PERIOD
200 B.C. - 1300 A.D.
O06279

Mining

In pre-Hispanic times, indigenous peoples in what is now known as Colombia wore ornaments made of gold, copper, platinum and, to a lesser extent, silver. The extraction of these metals acted as a stimulus to Spanish enterprise during the Conquest and the colonial era, with the result that interesting notes were left behind about places where native mining went on, and about the different types of mining activity. Panning is mentioned as having been the main way that gold was obtained from alluvial deposits on river beds; shafts up to six metres deep were also dug, as were irrigation ditches and canals, in order to divert water and thus make it easier for gold-bearing sands to be gathered, or to take water to an open seam and thus make it possible to wash and separate out the material. Other colonial texts describe the indigenous custom of hanging nets across the fast-flowing currents of rivers, so as to trap "nuggets" of the golden metal.

Miners are known to have dug shafts and canals with wooden clubs, the tips of which they hardened by fire, or with stone hammers and axes. They carried the mineral in baskets to the smelting sites, so it could be crushed, washed or cast. The indians combined these tasks with their domestic activities, and differentiated between mining work in the dry and the rainy seasons, because the chances of obtaining metals varied according to the amount of water at different times of the year. **JSS**

Indians panning for gold
*HISTORIA GENERAL Y NATURAL
DE LAS INDIAS*
GONZALO FERNÁNDEZ
DE OVIEDO   1535

Chisel with wooden handle
9.6 X 0.6 CM
PUPIALES, NARIÑO
NARIÑO HIGH PLAINS, LATE
PERIOD
1250 A.D.
O20127

Gold nugget from a
seam in Antioquia

16th century documents refer
to panning using wooden trays

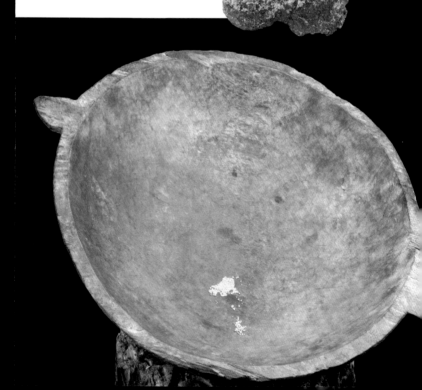

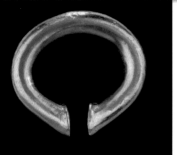

Nose ring
3 X 3.4 CM
PACIFIC COAST, TUMACO
INGUAPÍ PERIOD
700 B.C. - 350 A.D.
O05141

Metalworking Techniques
By Hammer and Fire

Because they are malleable and ductile, gold, copper and silver can be stretched out into sheets or threads. These metals have an atomic structure in the form of crystals with parallel planes, and when these are struck by a hammer, they move. But repeated blows distort the crystals so much that they hinder the sliding movement of the planes, cause tensions which harden the sheet, and lead to fractures occurring instead of stretching. The metal has to be heated until it turns bright red, so that the crystals can get back to their correct positions, the metal becomes malleable once more, and hammering can continue. This annealing process has to be repeated fairly frequently.

To make sheets, pre-Hispanic metalsmiths hit rounded ingots against stone slabs or anvils. They used hammers of different shapes, materials, sizes and weights, depending on the alloy, the size of the object, or the phase of the work.

Earring cover
5 X 8.4 CM
PACIFIC COAST,
TUMACO INGUAPÍ
PERIOD
700 B.C. - 350 A.D.
O29253

20

Polishing instruments carved from igneous rock

There is a particularly hard, heavy hammer in the Gold Museum collection, which was made of iron found in nature.

shape. Awls, embossers or engravers' chisels enhanced embossed designs, while stone polishers provided the surface finish, smoothing out and correcting any imperfections. **JSS**

HOW PLATINUM WAS USED

The only places in America where platinum was used in metallurgy were the Tumaco - La Tolita region on Colombia's Pacific Coast, and in Ecuador, where alluvial deposits are found in abundance, together with gold. The high fusion point of platinum (1,770°C) meant that it was beyond the technological skills of the different indigenous groups, and so metalsmiths developed the sintering technique: when grains of platinum mixed with gold are heated, the gold melts and traps the platinum; the resulting ingot can then be worked by hammering. Depending on the proportion of platinum used, the ornament that was produced was more or less silver in colour. **JSS**

The metallographic microscope shows grains of platinum surrounded by cast gold

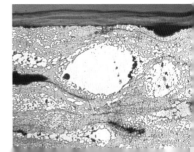

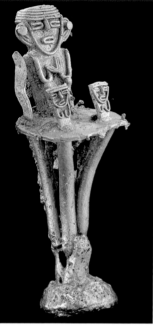

**Votive figure shaped
like an enclosure**
12.8 X 4.5 CM
PASCA, CUNDINAMARCA
EASTERN CORDILLERA, MUISCA
PERIOD.
600 A.D. - 1600 A.D.
O15117

**Ceramic mould
for metalwork**
5.8 X 3.8 CM
CARIBBEAN PLAINS,
LATE ZENÚ
1000 A.D. - 1600 A.D.
C12538

From Wax to Metal

One notable feature of Colombian pre-Hispanic goldwork was the predominant role that was played by casting using the lost wax method. Metalsmiths were masters at making ornaments and containers in wax with their hands and then transforming them into metal. They knew where and how to collect beeswax, they understood what type of clay was most suitable for making the casting moulds, and they were capable of handling the necessary temperatures for casting each metal or its alloys. The wax was obtained from beehives that housed bees with no sting (*Trigona (Tetragonisca) angustula*), a species that is particularly common in Colombian rainforests.

Once the desired figure had been modelled in wax, a number of rolls of the same material were added to it, to form the channels that the metal would flow through. The wax model was coated with successive layers of clay, to form a mould. When the mould dried, it was heated, so that the wax would melt and could be removed, and while the mould was still very hot, liquid metal was poured into it at the necessary temperature and in the required quantity, so that it completely filled the empty shape of the original mould. When the mould was cold, the goldsmith had to brake it to remove the metal figure, cut the channels and polish it. Since the model and the mould were destroyed, each cast object is a unique work of pre-Hispanic art. **J S S**

**Lime container shaped
like a calabash**
18 X 18.5 CM
PUERTO NARE,
ANTIOQUIA
MID-CAUCA, EARLY
PERIOD
500 B.C. - 700 A.D.
032854

**Lime stick with
anthropomorphous
head**
31.5 X 1.7 CM
CALIMA REGION,
YOTOCO PERIOD
200 B.C. - 1300 A.D.
004648

TWIN-METAL PINS

Twin-metal pins, which were made in the Calima
region during the Yotoco Period, are masterpieces of
Colombian pre-Hispanic metalwork, and their form and
the manufacturing technique employed make them
unique in America. The use of different alloys at various
stages in the casting process and a mastery of the
different temperatures at which the metals were cast
meant that articulated or dual-coloured pinheads could
be produced.

Small gold objects that had been made beforehand
were included in the wax model, in the shape of the final
figure. The model, complete with its clay mould coating,
was then cast using the lost wax method, with care being
taken to pour in an alloy that had a lower fusion point
than gold. On anthropomorphous pinheads, the dark-
skinned character thus shows off his golden outfit. **JSS**

Textures, Shines and Colours. Managing Surfaces

The Colour of the Sun

Tumbaga, an intentional fusing of gold and copper, was the alloy that was most commonly used by pre-Hispanic metalsmiths in the territory now known as Colombia. By merging silver-bearing gold with differing proportions of copper, they produced a wide range of gold, silver and reddish tones, and they also manipulated the natural properties of the metals, such as the temperature that was needed for melting them, their hardness and their smell.

Irrespective of the amount of gold that was present in the alloy, the metalsmiths achieved golden tones with an intense shine, using the depletion gilding process.

When a tumbaga object is heated over a flame, the copper in the alloy oxidises and the oxides tend to come out, leaving the surface with a dark tone. The metalsmith removed these oxides with acid solutions such as that obtained from wild sorrel (*oxalis pubescens*). Gold does not oxidise, nor does it react with oxalic acid, so when the oxidised copper was removed, a fine gilded layer was left on the surface, and the metalsmith could make this as thick as he wanted, by repeating the process. Finally, this layer was polished, to seal the pores and give it a shine. **JSS**

Photograph enlarged 100 times, taken with a metallographic microscope. The gilded layer on each side indicates that the sheet was subjected to the depletion gilding process

Oxalis pubescens

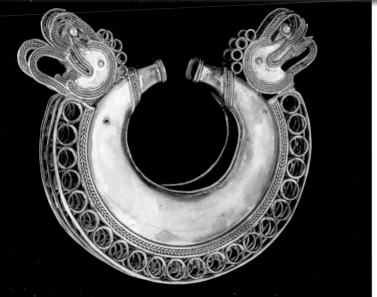

Half-moon shaped earring
with zoomorphous figures
7.7 X 10 CM
SIERRA NEVADA DE SANTA
MARTA, TAIRONA PERIOD
900 A.D. - 1600 A.D.
O25788

Zoomorphous pendant
5.3 X 3.7 CM
SIERRA NEVADA DE SANTA
MARTA, TAIRONA PERIOD
900 A.D. - 1600 A.D.
O19833

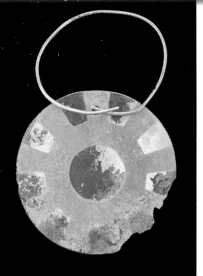

Earring Pendant
Ø 5.7 CM
NARIÑO HIGH
PLAINS, LATE
PERIOD
600 A.D.
- 1600 A.D.
022503

Contrasting Colours and Textures

Many ritual metal objects and ornaments on the Nariño High Plains were made from tumbaga that had a low gold content. The Nariño metalsmiths nevertheless gilded the surfaces and produced geometric designs which combined the pink tones of the alloy with the golden ones of the surface decoration, and shiny surfaces with opaque ones.

When the surface of an object had been gilded, certain areas marked out with geometric motifs were scraped with abrasive materials in order to remove the gilded layer and reveal the underlying copper colour of the alloy.

Once part of the design, which had been gilded and polished to a shine, had been kept separate with resins, the exposed surface was treated with a salt-based paste, which left it porous and opaque. With time, the porous surfaces made it easier for the copper in the alloy to oxidise internally, and this is why we see dark tones. **JSS**

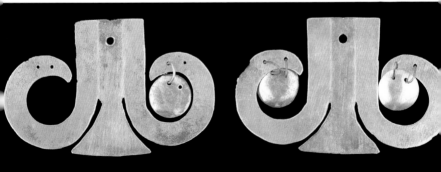

Appliqué work for textiles
• 4.0 X 6.3 CM   • 3.9 X 6.2 CM
PUPIALES, NARIÑO. NARIÑO HIGH PLAINS, LATE PERIOD
600 A.D. - 1600 A.D.
020965, 020966

**Rotating
Disk**
Ø 14.9 CM
PUPIALES,
NARIÑO
NARIÑO HIGH
PLAINS, LATE
PERIOD
600 A.D.
- 1600 A.D.
O21220

Ø 15.5 CM
EL TAMBO, NARIÑO
NARIÑO HIGH PLAINS,
LATE PERIOD
600 A.D. - 1600 A.D.
O21524

Deterioration of Artefacts

Ancient Repairs

Gold artefacts were highly valued by pre-Hispanic societies, because of both the meanings and stories attached to them and the material, knowledge and skill involved in working them. Many of these objects were therefore repaired by ancient goldsmiths. Some got damaged through constant use and were remade using wires, tapes or rivets, while others, which had manufacturing defects, were repaired using new metal pourings or, as in the case of the filigree earrings from the Caribbean Plains, by mending the weave with metal threads. **JSS**

>
Nose Ring
8.30 X 22 CM
RESTREPO,
VALLE DEL CAUCA
MID-CAUCA, LATE PERIOD
700 A.D. - 1600 A.D.
007944

Breastplate
Ø 18 CM
MID-CAUCA, LATE PERIOD
700 A.D. - 1600 A.D.
005957

Earrings
· 4.1 X 6.2 CM ·4.2 X 6.3 CM
SAN BENITO ABAD, SUCRE
CARIBBEAN PLAINS ZENÚ TRADITION
200 B.C. - 1600 A.D. O24157, O24156

OXIDES WHICH LEAVE THEIR MARK

Many ornaments were made in the past from alloys consisting of silver-bearing gold and large quantities of copper. While the high purity gold rarely alters, copper and silver react chemically with oxygen, salts in the soil, and moisture. Man gets his raw materials from ores that he takes from nature and subjects to smelting processes in order to extract metal from them; but corrosion, which is a natural reaction between metal and the environment, fights to take metal back to its original state as ore. As corrosion progresses in an artefact, so the minerals increase in volume, deform the surface, and cover it with porous layers. **JSS**

Breastplate
REVERSE AND OBVERSE
Ø 22.8 CM
MID-CAUCA, LATE PERIOD
700 A.D. - 1600 A.D.
O28430

People and Gold in Pre-Hispanic Colombia

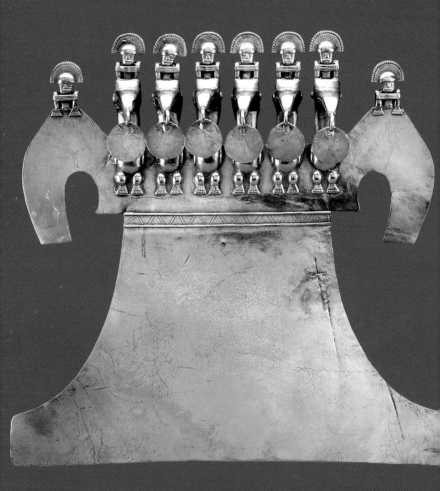

Bird-shaped breastplate with anthropomorphous figures
21 X 22.5 CM
GUATAVITA, CUNDINAMARCA
EASTERN CORDILLERA
MUISCA - GUANE PERIOD
600 A.D. - 1600 A.D.   O01253

2 0,000 EYARS AGO America was inhabited by hunters and gatherers who had crossed from the Old World. With the passing of time, many of them came to develop agriculture, to work clay, and to live in villages and towns. Metallurgy, which was discovered in Peru and Ecuador about 1,500 years before the Christian era, spread northwards to the south coast of Colombia, firstly, and then afterwards to the rest of this vast territory. Metalwork flourished in the Andean area and along the Colombian coasts from 500 B.C. to the time of the Spanish Conquest, in the 16th century. There were more than a dozen different styles and numerous societies, and this resulted in thousands of objects being made using varying techniques and forms, and in different metal alloys.

Metalwork was common in societies that had permanent political and religious leaders who governed groups of villages. Although they were not states, these chieftainships fed their large populations by virtue of an efficient agricultural system based on the growing of corn and cassava, coupled to the plentiful results of hunting and fishing activities. Because there were food surpluses, some people were able to engage in specialised activities such as religious worship, sculpture, the bartering of goods, mining and metalwork.

Metallurgical production existed to serve the ruling classes, who used large ornaments to reinforce their prestige and as a visible sign of their authority. These sacred, symbolic objects expressed a complex philosophy relating to the origin of the world and of mankind, one which explained the evolution of the universe and justified social and natural relationships. Ordinary people used numerous simple ornaments, too. Metals were also used for making tools that were used in everyday life and offerings which, when delivered up to the gods at rituals, enabled communities to preserve equilibrium in the cosmos. RLL

Metallurgy Chronology in Colombia

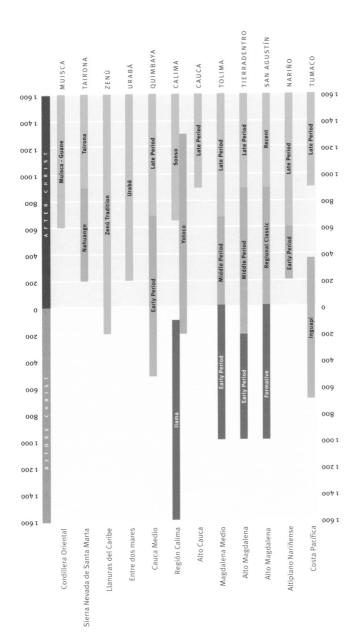

Archaeological Regions

Santa Marta
Barranquilla
Koguí
TAIRONA
Ijka
Cartagena
Yuko
ZENÚ
Cuna
URABÁ
Embera
Medellín
Uwa
QUIMBAYA
Bogotá
Sikuani
Guahibo
Noanama
Pijao
MUISCA
Cali
CALIMA
MALAGANA
TOLIMA
TIERRADENTRO
Cubeo
TUMACO
SAN AGUSTÍN
NARIÑO
Pasto
Sibundoy
Desana
Kofán
Tucano
Barasana
Makuna
Uitoto
Tikuna

Arqueological regions

Current ethnic groups

○ Cities

Nariño High Plains - Nariño

Lofty volcanoes, cold high plains and hot intermontane valleys make up the Andean landscape in Colombia's southern Nariño region and in Carchí province across the border in Ecuador. This vastly-contrasting terrain was home to numerous societies who were highly skilled in pottery and the working of metals for more than a thousand years.

Groups of farmers, llama herders and merchants inhabited the region from at least 600 A.D., and built their huts on the mountains and on gently sloping hillsides, as well as in flat places that were suitable for growing crops.

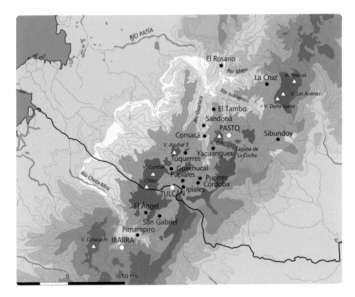

> Area around Galeras volcano, Nariño High Plains

In the middle of the 16th century, the Spaniards arrived from Quito and found numerous societies, including Pastos, Quillacingas, Sindaguas, Abades, Mocoas and Sucumbíos. The Pastos surprised the Spaniards because there were so many of them, because they controlled agriculture at different climatic levels, and because of the extensive network of trails that the *mindalaes,* or specialist traders, travelled along to barter exotic products like sea snails, alluvial gold, chonta palm wood, cotton, and beads from the *Spondylus* shell. Some of these societies still live in the region today, and are fighting to keep their customs and traditions alive. **LAG**

Breastplate with
anthropomorphous figure.
13.7 CM
MIRAFLORES, PUPIALES, NARIÑO.
NARIÑO HIGH PLAINS,
LATE PERIOD.
600 A.D. - 1600 A.D.
O20111

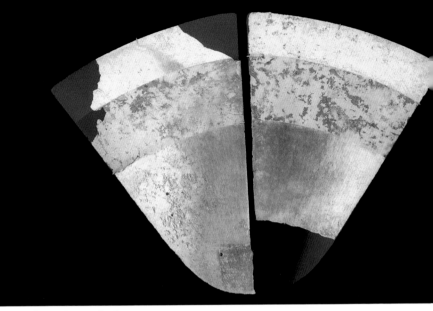

Diadem imitating feathers
24 X 18.1 CM
PUPIALES, NARIÑO
NARIÑO HIGH PLAINS, LATE PERIOD
600 A.D. - 1600 A.D.
022495, 033464

A Hierarchical Society

Interpretations of archaeological records point to a highly hierarchical society having lived in southern Nariño and in Carchí province in Ecuador from at least the 6th century until the end of the 15th century. The elite reinforced and established their power by exchanging exotic products with the inhabitants of the Pacific Coast and the dense jungles of Putumayo.

As with other societies in the central Andes, this one had a dual conception of life and the world, where things were thought of as being a union of opposing yet complementary parts, where one could not exist without the other. In the political field, this binary thought logic expressed itself in the form of a diarchy: in other words, there were two main leaders, simultaneously.

The two power groups were notable for their use of emblems made of metal, clay, stone and wood. One of

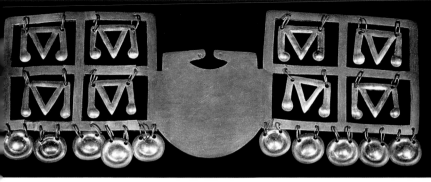

Nose ring with horizontal extensions
8.4 X 23.2 CM
PUPIALES, NARIÑO
NARIÑO HIGH
PLAINS, LATE PERIOD
600 A.D. - 1600 A.D.
O16631

Female anthropomorphous figure
15.5 X 12 CM
LA VICTORIA, IPIALES, NARIÑO.
NARIÑO HIGH PLAINS,
LATE PERIOD
600 A.D. - 1600 A.D.
C03097

Male anthropomorphous figure
18.3 X 13 CM
NARIÑO HIGH PLAINS,
LATE PERIOD
600 A.D. - 1600 A.D.
C05583

Breastplate in the form of a schematised bird
13.2 X 14.2 CM
PUPIALES, NARIÑO
NARIÑO
HIGH PLAINS, LATE
PERIOD
600 A.D.
- 1600 A.D.
O30127

them wore objects in which abstract forms and geometric designs predominated, while the other identified itself by means of insignia that had figurative designs, with anthropomorphous depictions and stylised monkeys and birds. Despite the major differences in techniques, forms and designs, an iconographic and technological unity can be appreciated. **LAG**

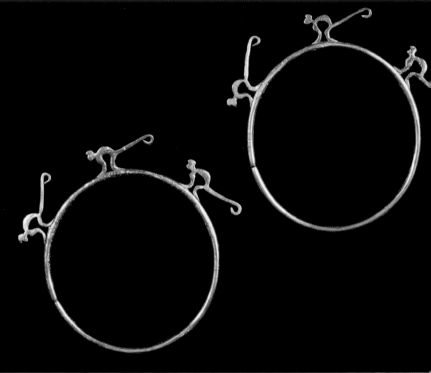

Earrings with zoomorphous figures
10 AND 10.4 CM   GUACHUCAL, NARIÑO
NARIÑO HIGH PLAINS, LATE PERIOD
600 A.D. - 1600 A.D.
O22041, O22042

SYMMETRY AND MOVEMENT

Artefacts from the Nariño High Plains are fascinating, from an artistic viewpoint. Nose rings explore an art that is non-figurative, abstract, and which plays with geometry, with opposites like full and empty, and with movable pieces that make sounds and sparkle and twinkle in the light. The disks that hung from a cord and rotated were a forerunner, ten centuries ago, of kinetic art. In the abstract birds with forked tails, perhaps frigate birds, the proportions of the human figure as drawn by Leonardo Da Vinci can be sensed. Nariño art equally insists on the qualities of equilibrium and perfection that symmetry provides. It is therefore surprising to find two asymmetrical earrings with three monkeys on top of them who never stop jumping and turning, playing with rhythm and almost with music, to create the illusion of movement. **EL**

Rotating Disks

A number of metal disks with an opening in the middle and perfect graphics in the form of geometric decoration on both faces consisting of lines, circles, triangles and spirals were found in deep tombs of important dignitaries. One still has a cotton cord in its central hole. In a society which sought to transcend to other levels of conscience through shamanism, the light effects and the sensation of movement that the disks give off as they rotate must have induced special mental states which the leading dignitaries could have used in order to reinforce their power and their magical-religious symbolism in ceremonies and rituals. **LAG**

Rotating disks
15 CM
MIRAFLORES VILLAGE, PUPIALES, NARIÑO
NARIÑO HIGH PLAINS, LATE PERIOD
600 A.D. - 1600 A.D.
O21222 / O21523

The Deepest Tombs in America

This society buried its leaders in individual and collective tombs that were sometimes as much as 40 metres deep. These are the deepest tombs in America. In ground consisting of unconsolidated volcanic rock, expert builders dug vertical shafts that ended in side chambers, the walls of which they painted red, perhaps as part of a ritual whose meaning has become lost with the passing of time. Laid out on the floor of the vault and adorned with sumptuous ornaments, the corpses were wrapped in blankets and placed on mats woven from vegetable fibres. Objects with a deep symbolic content, such as sea snails, *Spondylus* necklaces,

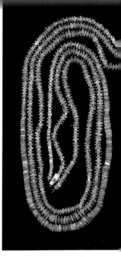

Necklace made of cylindrical beads
2.1 X 1.3 CM
NARIÑO HIGH PLAINS,
LATE PERIOD
600 A.D. - 1600 A.D.
K01110

rotating disks made of gold, silver or tumbaga, llama hair fabrics, wigs made of human hair and iron pyrite mirrors were deposited as offerings in a hole or depression that was dug in the floor, in the middle of the vault.

These deep funerary structures which housed leaders after their death entailed a major investment in terms of communal work in removing earth, preparing the deceased, and organising and holding funeral ceremonies and dances. They differ from the tombs of ordinary people, which were only one or two metres deep and often contained nothing more than a rough clay vessel, a stone axe or other artefact, and sometimes a simple, metal nose ring. **LAG**

Amphora
63.2 X 24 CM
NARIÑO HIGH PLAINS, LATE PERIOD
600 A.D. - 1600 A.D.
C12861

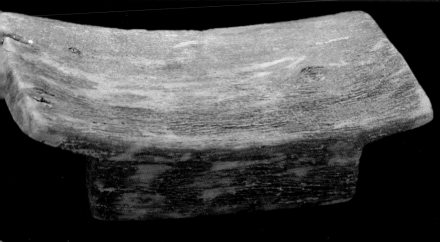

Bench
28 X 13.5 CM
GUAITARILLA, NARIÑO
NARIÑO HIGH PLAINS, LATE PERIOD
600 A.D. - 1600 A.D.
M00020

Iron pyrite mirror
5 X 4.9 CM
TÚQUERRES, NARIÑO.
NARIÑO HIGH PLAINS, LATE PERIOD
600 A.D. - 1600 A.D.
L03411

SHAFT TOMBS IN AMERICA

Archaeological research has recorded shaft tombs
with side chambers from Mexico right down to Chile.
Examples of this type of tomb exist with rectangular,
square, elliptical, semi-elliptical and oval chambers, and
with shafts ranging from one or two to forty metres
deep, such as those recorded in southern Nariño and in
Carchí province in Ecuador. The shape and design of the
chamber often recall homes, suggesting that people
believed in life after death. **LAG**

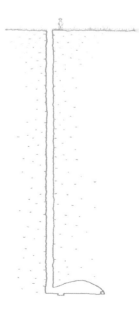

Cultural Diversity: Pastos and Quillacingas

The Andean territory where the Pastos lived was notable for its wide range of bio-climatic levels and varied ecosystems, and for its closeness to the wetlands and jungles of the Amazon and the Pacific. Pasto societies developed a small-scale, vertical, land management system, and had trading and bartering relationships with neighbouring groups.

This micro-vertical management consisted of exploiting various climatic levels that were no more than a day's walk from each other, so they could stock up on cold-climate products like potatoes, quinoa, ocas and ollucos, along with ones from hot regions, such as fruit and various types of corn.

Salt, coca, chili, sisal, cotton and other products were bartered through groups of native Pastos who lived permanently outside their region on land they shared with other communities. These multi-ethnic territories also acted as market centres, to which *mindalaes*, or specialist merchants, flocked on long-distance bartering missions, enabling the Pastos to build up stocks of the exotic products and goods that the elite required for maintaining their power.

In Quillacinga territory, communities settled in scattered groups on mountain slopes and on flat land where they could grow corn, which was their main source of sustenance. These communities were organised around a main lord, although their social structure was less firm and coherent than that of their neighbours, the Pastos. They buried their dead in rectangular shaft tombs with side chambers, accompanied by a pottery offering and simple metal nose rings. **L A G**

Breastplate
15.6 CM
QUILLACINGA
1300 A.D. - 1700 A.D.
O24485

Vessel with geometric decoration
24.9 X 34.5 CM
QUILLACINGA
1300 A.D. - 1700 A.D.
C09096

Half-moon shaped nose ring
5.2 X 5.6 CM
QUILLACINGA
1300 A.D. - 1700 A.D.
O30779

Vessel with anthropomorphous figure
13.2 X 27.3 CM
QUILLACINGA
1300 A.D. - 1700 A.D.
C05455

THE ART OF WEAVING

Nariño was the only part of the country where people wove with the wool of the American camel, where metal baskets were made, and where wigs were woven and plaited with human hair. Various vegetable dyes were used in the weaving of camel-wool (probably alpaca) blankets, in order to obtain colours like red, yellow, brown, grey and black. The geometric designs that decorated textiles, such as the staggered line motif, can often also be found in pottery and goldwork from this region. Carbon 14 analyses have enabled it to be established that both camel-wool and cotton textiles were made around the year 1000 A.D. **LAG**

THE FOOD OF THE GODS

Quinoa (*Chenopodium quinua*), a grass which present-day Andean societies consider to be a sacred food, was domesticated somewhere on the arid high plains of the Andes at least 4,000 years ago. This cereal, which has a high protein, carbohydrate, mineral and vitamin content, was eaten in pre-Hispanic times in the form of tortillas, tamales, bread, biscuits and soups. Recent studies have rated it one of the best vegetable-origin foods for human consumption. **LAG**

Rattles
· 3.8 X 3.5 CM
· 5.4 X 5.4 CM
NARIÑO HIGH PLAINS, LATE PERIOD
600 A.D. - 1600 A.D.
019662 / 025201

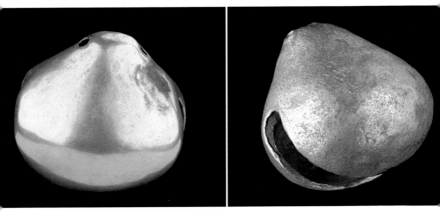

Music and Ritual

Pan's pipes, trumpets, maracas and rattles were played by the pre-Hispanic inhabitants of the high plains of Nariño and Carchi.

In the symbolic thought of Amerindian societies, the gods created music and dance and gave them to man, to accompany him in his most transcendental activities. Sowing and harvesting ceremonies, initiation rites, healing and death, and activities like marriages and births, were collective events where music and dance played a prominent role.

The coordinated movements of musicians in rounds, dances and rituals can be seen depicted on clay vessels painted black and red on a cream background.

Their dual conception of the world was also apparent in musical creation.

Pan's Pipes
16.6 X 8.2 CM
MIRAFLORES VILLAGE, PUPIALES, NARIÑO.
NARIÑO HIGH PLAINS, LATE PERIOD
600 A.D. - 1600 A.D.
O23666

• 19,8 X 6,6 CM.
NARIÑO HIGH PLAINS, LATE PERIOD
600 A.D. - 1600 A.D.
O19658

Two Pan's pipes - male and female - form a single Andean instrument, where each part is considered to be the complementary half of the other. They are played by two musicians, who alternate by mutual agreement as they play the notes of the different melodies. The metalsmiths of Nariño and Carchi stressed this dual concept by making flutes of gold and silver, metals that were associated with male and female duality, and with the mythical couple formed by the Sun and the Moon. **LAG**

Pacific Coast. Tumaco - La Tolita

Archaeological evidence of the Tumaco - La Tolita tradition has been found along Colombia's Pacific Coast region from Esmeraldas in Ecuador to Bocana, in Buenaventura, Colombia. It dates back to more than 700 B.C., and relates to metalworking societies organised under chieftainships that lived off the mangrove swamps and tropical jungle, which provided them with abundant natural resources. Fishermen, hunters and farmers sailed the coasts and into the plains to get food, which consisted of fruit and sea food, as archaeological research has revealed. They continued to live there until 350 A.D. Other groups of humans, who left behind no evidence of metalworking activities, settled later on El Morro island and on the coastal plain, and remained there until the Conquest. **S M V**

> Mangroves at
> Tumaco, on the
> Pacific Coast

> Mask
> 29.9 X 21.6 CM
> PACIFIC COAST,
> INGUAPÍ PERIOD
> 700 B.C. - 350 A.D.
> O29480

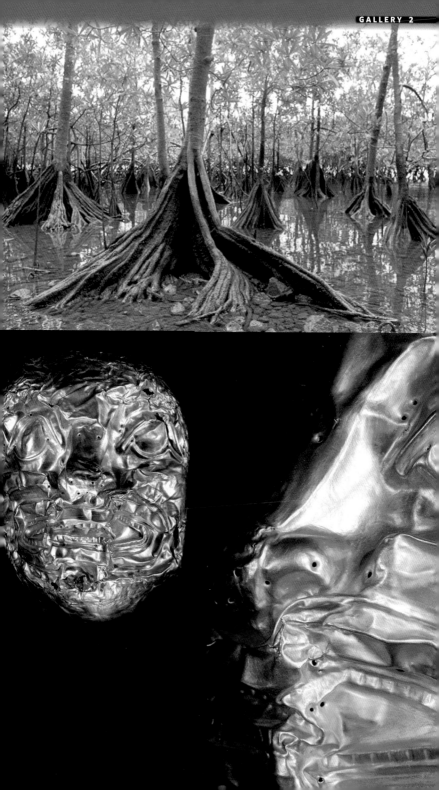

The People of the Mangrove Swamps

The coastal plain boasts an intricate natural system of channels and estuaries that links the coast with the mainland. The people who lived there were excellent sailors who travelled in small canoes, with the help of the tides, all along the estuaries and waterways.

Figure in the form of a canoe
3.9 X 14.9 CM
PACIFIC COAST,
INGUAPÍ PERIOD
700 B.C. - 350 A.D.
C13522

This watery environment provided them with molluscs, crustaceans, fish and birds in abundance, as well as a number of mammals that could be hunted. Evidence exists of corn and cassava crops having been grown from 1000 A.D. onwards, on plots around homes and on large platforms, with canals, trenches, ridges and drainage ditches.

Objects like stone weights for nets, hooks made of gold and shells, and pottery de-scalers bear testimony to their fishing and mollusc-gathering activities.

Housing and burial sites are on artificial mounds that were built on small islets formed by sand deposits in marshy areas inside the mangrove swamps. Houses were generally rectangular or square with gabled roofs, as depicted on their pottery, and some were used for ritual or ceremonial purposes. Remains of adobe, sometimes with bamboo marks imprinted in them, have been found on archaeological digs. **S M V**

Figure in the form of a house
12.2 X 12.5 CM
PACIFIC COAST, INGUAPÍ
PERIOD
700 B.C. - 350 A.D.
C05683

Pendant
1.3 X 2.7 CM
PACIFIC COAST,
INGUAPÍ PERIOD
700 B.C. - 350 A.D.
033606

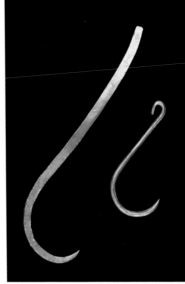

Hooks
3.5 CM 7.2 X 2.3 CM
PACIFIC COAST,
INGUAPÍ PERIOD
700 B.C. - 350 A.D.
001172, 006560

MANGROVES

Vegetation groups that are found
in coastal areas in the tropics and
sub-tropics. They consist of woodland
where red mangrove and black
mangrove predominate; these are
woody species that are notable for
the way they have adapted to living in
brackish water in areas that mark the
boundary between land and sea. They

Black Mangrove
Aviceumia germinans

can anchor themselves to light sediments, and they have respiratory roots and
special mechanisms for withstanding salt water. They form a bridge between salt
and fresh water, and fish, crustaceans, molluscs and the birds that feed off these
marine, estuary and lake resources abound in such marshy zones. **SMV**

49

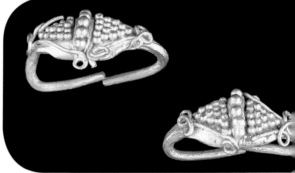

Earring pendants
10.8 CM
TUMACO, NARIÑO
PACIFIC COAST,
INGUAPÍ PERIOD.
700 B.C. - 350 A.D.
032949 /032950

Earrings
· 3.3 X 1.6 CM
· 3.3 X 1.4 CM
PACIFIC COAST,
INGUAPÍ PERIOD.
700 B.C. - 350 A.D.
033853 / 033854

The Language of the Figurines

The fact that human figures are a recurring theme in archaeological digs on rubbish dumps and mounds, or are simply found exposed on the surface, leads to the idea that they were made for ritual purposes connected with the supernatural world and activities in everyday life. Some archaeologists have suggested that because they have been found broken and on rubbish dumps, they were deliberately destroyed when they no longer had any sacred value. This is what happens in the ritual practices of certain present-day indigenous communities, who portray in their ceremonies the spirits that accompany the shaman or the evils that afflict the sick in the form of wooden figures. They destroy these when the ceremony ends, to prevent the evils or sickness that remain in them from affecting another member of the community.

Some Tumaco figures depict warriors, shamans, dancers and probably chieftains, all of them richly attired and wearing ornaments which stress the

Anthropomorphous figure
14.1 X 7.2 CM
PACIFIC COAST,
INGUAPÍ PERIOD.
700 B.C. - 350 A.D.
C13445

**Anthropomorphous
figure**
52.5 X 26 CM
TUMACO, NARIÑO
PACIFIC COAST,
INGUAPÍ PERIOD.
700 B.C. - 350 A.D.
C12819

power they must have held when they were alive. The plasticity of the clay and the skill of the potters gave the figures movement, details and individual features, and even suggest that they could have been portraits of leading dignitaries. Gestures, postures and emotions were all etched in them, as evidence of the lives and everyday activities of their creators.

The tension in the body, the angle of the face, the arms resting on the legs, or the hands holding the jaw, all these features seem to get across states of meditation, tiredness, or quiet hope. And in addition to these fine details, there are gestures like knitted brows, expectant eyes and half-open mouths, or exalted muscles, wrinkles or bones. **S M V**

Masked dignitary
26.3 X 16.4 CM
NARIÑO
PACIFIC COAST, INGUAPÍ
PERIOD.
700 B.C. - 350 A.D.
C01587

Anthropomorphous figure
10.5 X 10.5 CM
TUMACO, NARIÑO
PACIFIC COAST, INGUAPÍ
PERIOD.
700 B.C. - 350 A.D.
C12762

Roller
3.9 X 6.3 CM
PACIFIC COAST, INGUAPÍ
PERIOD.
700 B.C. - 350 A.D.
C05695

Stamp with zoomorphous design
7.4 X 11 CM
PACIFIC COAST, INGUAPÍ PERIOD.
700 B.C. - 350 A.D.
C05726

STAMPS ON THE SKIN

Most Tumaco pottery figures were painted, but the paint has worn off. Because of the large numbers of stamps and rollers that have been found, we know that for religious or everyday purposes, bodies were adorned with rhombuses, squares and schematised figures that could have had some ethnic or hierarchical relevance or have referred to civil status. Organic dyes such as red annatto or black genipap also served the function that sunblocks and insect repellents do today.

SMV

Stamp
4.3 X 8.4. CM
PACIFIC COAST, INGUAPÍ
PERIOD.
700 B.C. - 350 A.D.
C05729

The Life Cycle

The diversity that exists in the pottery figures enables the very cycle of existence to be told. The narrative commences with eroticism, the principle that brings about life. Faces in a state of ecstasy, voluptuous women in an attitude of yielding, phallic figures or suggestive postures in the game of love between the couple are clear evidence that sex was not reduced to the reproductive function, but rather had an unprejudiced, enjoyment value that was depicted aesthetically.

Faced with the restrictions imposed by the Spaniards, these peoples' sexual culture came to be expressed more naturally and with fewer inhibitions, as can be seen in objects where the phallus stands out as a symbol of fertility and a creator of life and power: it is even used as a handle in ceremonial containers, as a support in censers, or as a haft for rollers or de-scalers.

Life manifests itself in realistic figures depicting pregnancy, childbirth or lactation, and they bear testimony to the value that was placed on family life. Aging is personified by showing the effects that the passing of time has on the body, such as creased and wrinkled skin or hunched backs. Great importance must have been placed on the elderly for them to have been depicted so frequently.

Situations or problems of a sacred and natural order arise which interfere with the normal course of the life cycle, such as illnesses and genetic anomalies. We do not know how they viewed the sick, but we have evidence of the constant efforts that potters made to detail different pathologies. Past illnesses such as leishmaniasis of the skin, tuberculosis, syphilis, dwarfism, facial paralysis, Morquio's disease or Down's syndrome have all been diagnosed in their works.

Finally comes death, which was perceived as a process of gradually moving away from this world in order to go on living in the world of the dead. **S M V**

Phallic handle with anthropomorphous figure
9 X 28.5 CM   PACIFIC COAST, INGUAPÍ PERIOD.
700 B.C. - 350 A.D.   C13440

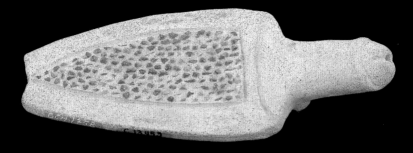

De-scaler
13.5 X 5.1 CM
PACIFIC COAST, INGUAPÍ PERIOD.
700 B.C. - 350 A.D.
C13453

Figure showing a woman lactating
16.8 X 9.3 CM
PACIFIC COAST, INGUAPÍ PERIOD.
700 B.C. - 350 A.D.
C09578

Anthropomorphous figure
31 X 20.8 CM
PACIFIC COAST,
INGUAPÍ PERIOD.
700 B.C. - 350 A.D.
C13436

Calima Region

The term Calima has been used since the colonial era to refer to the wide valley of the upper Calima River in the Eastern Cordillera, and the surrounding area. However, archaeologists use the word today to denote a wider area, one which also includes the upper parts of the towns of Yotoco and Vijes, the town of Restrepo, and Palmira and Cerrito on the flat soils of the Cauca valley. This region, with its temperate climate, boasts plentiful sources of water and gentle, rolling hills that repeatedly get fertilised by ash from the volcanoes in the Central Cordillera. It is not hard to see the remains of almost 9,000 years of habitation: ancient houses, fields where crops were grown, cemeteries and paths that were trodden by societies who were initially hunters and gatherers and then later, farmers, potters and metalsmiths. Archaeologists divide this history into periods that have been given the names Pre-Ceramic, Ilama, Yotoco-Malagana and Sonso. **JSP**

> Nose ring in the shape
> of a feline figure
> 22.1 X 21.1 CM
> RESTREPO, VALLE DEL
> CAUCA
> CALIMA, YOTOCO
> PERIOD.
> 200 B.C. - 1300 A.D.
> O16637

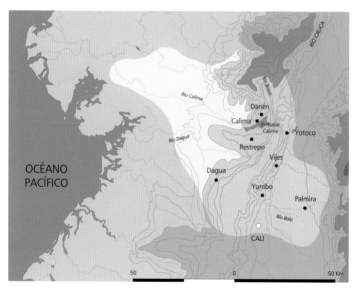

> El Dorado Valley in
> Valle del Cauca

People in the Ilama Period

The potters of the Ilama Period, which dates back to 1600 years before Christ, were able to capture evidence of their world in pottery. It was an idealised world, one that was modelled in pottery containers and objects, where men with enormous baskets lived alongside women who engaged in a variety of different duties and animals that were sometimes little more than sketched in by the skilled craftsmen. Most of these objects were found in tombs, where they formed part of the funerary attire of leading dignitaries whose social identity we can today only infer from their offerings. The thick lips and the large, aquiline noses, not to mention the robust appearance of many of the figures, no doubt suggest clearly-defined ideal types of person and aesthetic standards of beauty and personal adornment. People's eyes, elongated like coffee beans, differ from the rounded eyes of animals and beasts in this world that was rich in images. The "fabulous beast" which typifies the various beasts of this period combines human traits with elements from various animal species, such as feline figures, bats and snakes.

These fantastic creatures are perhaps an allusion to integration between human beings and nature, where humans take on characteristics that are typical of certain animals in order to symbolically acquire their power. At the same time, nature is incorporated into society by ascribing to animals traits that are typical of human, social behaviour, something that is commonly found amongst many indigenous communities today, for whom the boundaries between people and other beings in the natural world are very tenuous. The twin-spouted vessels known as *alcarrazas* combine these expressions of an ancient cultural tradition, and remind us that our view of the world is but one amongst many. **J S P**

Anthropomorphous vessel
12 X 7.3 CM
RESTREPO, VALLE DEL CAUCA
CALIMA, ILAMA PERIOD
1600 B.C. - 100 A.D.
C04534

Anthropomorphous
alcarraza
24 X 18.5 CM
CALIMA, ILAMA PERIOD
1600 B.C. - 100 A.D.
C00003

Alcarraza in the form
of an armadillo
20.4 X 14.4 CM
CALIMA, ILAMA PERIOD
1600 B.C. - 100 A.D.
C03184

People in the Yotoco Period

Near the end of the millennium before the birth of Christ, a new social order appears to have become established in the hot valleys of the Calima region, for reasons that are unknown to us. All we know are the results of those events: new shapes for artefacts, new materials, and above all, new symbols. During the period that archaeologists have called Yotoco - after the name of a town - inequalities were more pronounced between members of society. A leading group controlled works and harvest cycles, as well as the production and circulation of certain types of artefact, particularly gold ornaments. Although the pottery tradition

Reel-shaped earrings
- 6,2 X 6,2 CM
- 6,1 X 6,1 CM
RESTREPO, VALLE DEL CAUCA.
CALIMA, YOTOCO PERIOD.
200 B.C. - 1300 A.D.
O24929 /O24930

continued, albeit with a number of important changes, metal ornaments became the vehicle that was used for getting changes across.

The same enigmatic, repetitive face, which has come to be known as the Yotoco icon, is an outstanding feature of countless objects made of gold with a very high assay value. This iconic depiction of the human face is made up of various elements: a layered headdress, triangular or semi-circular eyes, straight nose, and a nose ring in the form of a feline figure on which the facial features of the icon - eyes, nose and mouth - are in turn repeated schematically, but with prominent canines and teeth that give it a threatening expression. For the societies that lived in the Calima region between 200 B.C. and 1300 A.D., this face, which was repeated time and time again on different objects, could have been specifically intended to express values, beliefs and aesthetic ideals, and it was perhaps a symbol of the power and rank of those who wore or were buried with gold ornaments. **JSP**

Heart-shaped breastplate
25.2 X 30.5 CM
RESTREPO, VALLE DEL
CAUCA.
CALIMA, YOTOCO PERIOD.
200 B.C. - 1300 A.D.
O05370

**Diadem with
anthropomorphous
figure and hanging
ornaments**
24.4 X 27.4 CM
CALIMA, YOTOCO PERIOD.
200 B.C. - 1300 A.D.
O23816

Ornament
22.1 X 13.4 CM
CALIMA, YOTOCO PERIOD.
200 B.C. - 1300 A.D.
O05753

The Chewing of Coca Leaves

No plant was more attractive to the peoples of ancient America than coca. The practice of chewing the leaves of this small *Erithroxylum* bush spread over a vast region, from the lofty high plains of the Andes to the depths of the Amazon jungle. The fact that in numerous places, objects have been found that were once used to help people achieve the potent effects of the sacred plant bears testimony to this ancient knowledge. Two typical utensils are required for chewing the *Erithroxylum novogranatense* variety: a *poporo* and a stick. The former is a container in which alkaline powder (lime from seashells) is kept; this helps release the components of the alkaloid when the roasted leaves are chewed. The stick, meanwhile, is used for taking this powder from the container to the mouth.

Calima - Malagana societies produced large quantities of different-shaped *poporos*. There are some that are in two parts, which are joined in the middle by hooks; in one, the upper part depicts an anthropomorphous figure while the lower part is shaped like the head of a crocodile which, because of its relatively wide, short snout, turned-up nose and clearly-defined eyelids, could be identified with a small alligator or *Caiman sclerops*. Others are shaped like marrows or corn cobs, and recall the relationship that exists between the shaman and nature, on the one hand, and on the other, the subject of fertility, which was so important in shamanistic thought. The lime sticks, meanwhile, have heads in the form of birds, bats, snakes, a mixture of various animals, or human figures with animals on the backs. Some of the characters depicted on the staff finials, which are delicately cast in gold with a high assay value, are wearing masks and items associated with ritual paraphernalia, thus recalling the sacred use to which this plant was put. **JSP**

>
Lime sticks
LEFT TO RIGHT
• 44.4 X 2.8 CM
ATACO, TOLIMA
CALIMA, YOTOCO PERIOD.
200 B.C. - 1300 A.D.
O05853
• 30 X 2.2 CM
RESTREPO,
VALLE DEL CAUCA
CALIMA, YOTOCO PERIOD.
200 B.C. - 1300 A.D.
O00026
• 31.5 X 1.6 CM
O05234
• 27.2 X 1.9 CM
O04252
• 29.6 X 1.7 CM
O03453

>
Phytomorphous lime containers
• 7.1 X 5.4 CM
CALIMA, YOTOCO PERIOD.
200 B.C. - 1300 A.D.
O05564

• 5.3 X 2.8 CM
PALMIRA,
VALLE DEL CAUCA
CALIMA,
MALAGANA PERIOD.
200 B.C. - 200 A.D.
O33204

Masks
FROM LEFT TO RIGHT AND TOP TO BOTTOM
PALMIRA, VALLE DEL CAUCA
CALIMA, MALAGANA PERIOD. 200 B.C. - 200 A.D.
• 26.3 X 41.4 CM O33337   • 29.5 X 53 CM O33407
• 29.7 X 49 CM O33403   • 25 X 30.5 CM O33196

Malagana. Funeral Masks

A cemetery that was discovered in 1992 revealed the existence of a society governed by chieftains that lived alongside Yotoco period societies from at least 200 B.C. to 200 A.D. Most of the tombs on Malagana estate contained numerous objects made of gold that had been buried as part of the funerary attire of the people interred there. Outstanding amongst these are the funeral masks that covered the faces of certain leading figures. Four gold masks were found in one of the tombs, three of them superimposed on the face of the deceased and the other on his feet. Some of them were found bent, because they had been fitted over the faces of the persons buried, suggesting that they were made exclusively to be buried with the person. Some depict various types of headdresses, in the form of strings of triangles, rectangles with embossed geometric designs or fungus-shaped extensions, and generally they have a characteristic rectangular mouth with two big lines of teeth. Made of gold with a high assay value, they symbolise death. Sometimes they resemble skulls, and at others, lifeless faces. **JSP**

The Looting of Malagana Cemetery

Malagana is the name of an estate, or hacienda, near the town of Palmira, on the fertile alluvial plains in the flat valley of the River Cauca. An indigenous cemetery was discovered there by chance in 1992, and the sumptuous gold funerary attires in the tombs there quickly caught the attention of grave plunderers, dealers in archaeological objects, and the local peasantry. The archaeological site was completely destroyed over a period of several months of unrestrained looting, meaning that the opportunity was lost for ever of learning a very important part of the history of the people who made those extraordinary objects. The fragile nature of the country's architectural heritage and the need for stronger mechanisms to protect it was made clear yet again. **JSP**

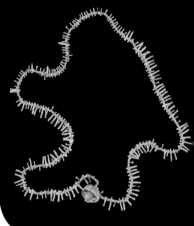

THE PASSION FLOWER

Images of flowers are very rare in Colombian pre-Hispanic metalwork. The pendant on this necklace is exceptional amongst the objects found in Malagana cemetery, because of the naturalism and faithfulness of the representation. There can be no doubt but that it is a passion flower, a member of the *Passiflora* family. Each of the three parts of this pendant - the pistil, the stamen and the petals - was cast separately and then assembled to make up the whole. A small stone fixes the outer part of the flower firmly in place. Many species of passion flower contain alkaloids that possess the principal features of *ayahuasca* or *yagé*, the sacred liana. **JSP**

Necklace with pendant in the form of a flower
3.2 X 2.5 CM
PALMIRA, VALLE DEL CAUCA
CALIMA,
MALAGANA PERIOD.
200 B.C. - 200 A.D.
O33277

Funerary Expressions: Ilama to Sonso

There are few activities that say so much about a society's ideology and the relations between its members as how they treat their dead. In order to understand what the world of the dead meant to pre-Hispanic societies, archaeologists analyse the objects they placed in their tombs as funerary attire, the forms and shapes of these, and the positions of the bodies and offerings. Groups of tombs in cemeteries are relatively common in the Calima region, but they have unfortunately been looted by treasure hunters. During the Ilama and Yotoco periods, tombs were dug that consisted of a shaft one or two metres

deep, with a small chamber or niche running off this in which the body and offerings were placed. Because of the acidity of the soils, the bones have disappeared after centuries of burial, and this has made it impossible to discover what people's physical features were like.

Sarcophagus carved from a tree shaft
220 X 52 CM
CALIMA,
PERÍODO SONSO
650 D.C. - 1600 D.C.
M00124

Archaeological evidence points to various changes having taken place from 650 A.D. onwards in the shape of tombs and the way in which the dead were treated. In the new period, called the Sonso Period, the deceased were buried in tombs up to fifteen metres deep with wide chambers, in sarcophagi carved from the trunks of tall trees, and sometimes there were even collective burials. Sarcophagi seem to have been reserved for certain leading figures, although their social identity is unknown today. Small wooden benches, trays, spades, lances and darts have survived, together with the sarcophagi, because the tombs were flooded with stagnant water, and this did not allow wood-eating bacteria to reproduce. **J S P**

Seeds and a carved wooden object
found inside the sarcophagus

THE RESTORATION OF A SARCOPHAGUS

One of the most interesting tasks undertaken
by the Gold Museum's restoration and
conservation team was to excavate the contents of a wooden sarcophagus from
the Calima region that was probably used during the Sonso Period (650 to 1700
A.D.). Seeds of various plants, such as cotton, maize, bean, chili and annatto, were
found in the earth that was still inside it, together with fragments of textiles and
a small figure carved out of wood. The researchers were particularly intrigued
by the fact that ferns were found, as these had seemingly been used as part of
the deathbed. The fibres of some species of fern are used today by peasants
and indigenous peoples to stuff pillows and mattresses, and these are known as
"mattresses of the poor". **J S P**

Upper Magdalena – San Agustín

The Colombian massif around the headwaters of the River Magdalena is a region of numerous ecological environments, ranging from snow-capped peaks to hot valleys. The landscape is rugged in the highest parts, and undulating in the alluvial valleys. The rivers that rush down from Papas Valley and other moorland areas are fast-flowing and have carved out deep canyons, narrow valleys like those of the Quinchana, Mazamorras and Bordones rivers, and waterfalls such as the one at Chaquira. Sometimes they flow through narrow, rocky gorges, like the one formed by the Magdalena at El Estrecho. By way of contrast, gently undulating hills are to be found in the temperate and cold zones. It is there, at heights of between 1,500 and 2,000 metres above sea level, that the majority of the population has always settled, attracted by the temperate climate with its average temperature of 18°C. The mountainous regions of San Agustín and the La Plata valley were inhabited continuously from 1000 B.C. to the time of the Spanish Conquest, but in different ways. During the Formative, Regional Classical and Recent periods, societies of farmers, potters and sculptors increased gradually in number and settled in ever more centralised villages. **J S P**

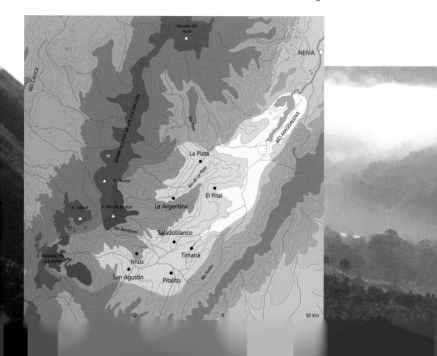

Statue
110 X 70 CM
SAN AGUSTÍN,
HUILA
UPPER
MAGDALENA –
SAN AGUSTÍN,
REGIONAL
CLASSICAL PERIOD
1 A.D. – 900 A.D.
L01336

Boundaries of
Tolima and Huila
in the valley
of the River
Magdalena

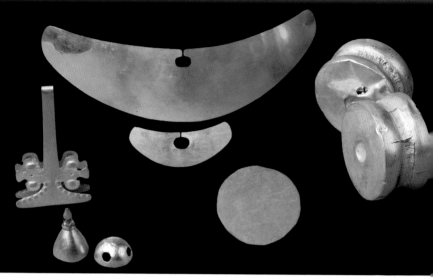

Chieftains, Statues and Funerary Attire during the Regional Classical Period

The San Agustín region is well-known for its statues and funeral shrines. These monumental public works were built for leading dignitaries in the Regional Classical Period, between 1 A.D. and 900 A.D. The iconography of the persons depicted on the statues suggests that those leaders were closely linked to religious practices, rituals, spiritual power and ideology. One notable feature of this period, in fact, is that the population was concentrated in and centralised around religious centres. However, it was not only in the monumental nature of the monoliths that the power of the leading dignitaries manifested itself, since a further outstanding feature is the delicate, artistic and highly individual manner in which ornaments for personal use were made.

The so-called winged fish funerary attire, which was found in the town of San Agustín, consists of a pendant in the form of a fish, two half-moon shaped nose rings, a pendant in the form of tweezers, a circular plate, two reel earrings and a small globular object with lid, the function of which is unknown. This funerary attire is believed to have belonged to an important member of the ruling elite during the Regional Classical Period, in societies that are referred to as chieftainships in archaeological literature, because of their complex social and economic organisation. **J S P**

Winged fish funeral attire
SAN AGUSTÍN, HUILA.
UPPER MAGDALENA - SAN AGUSTÍN,
REGIONAL CLASSICAL PERIOD.
1 A.D. - 900 A.D.

Reel-shaped earrings
6.5 X 3.8 CM
O32917, O32918
Half-moon shaped nose ring
5.6 X 21.8 CM
O32919
Half-moon shaped nose ring
2.4 X 7 CM
O32920
Pendant in the form of tweezers
8.4 X 5 CM
O32921
Circular plate
0 X 5.3 CM
O32922
Conical rattle
4.6 X 2.3 CM
O32923

Alcarraza in the shape of a house
7.7 X 12 CM
SAN AGUSTÍN, HUILA.
SAN AGUSTÍN, REGIONAL CLASSICAL PERIOD.
1 A.D. - 900 A.D.
C12829

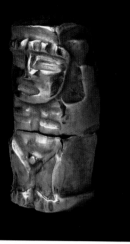

Anthropomorphous figure that looks like a statue
3.5 X 1.5 CM
SAN AGUSTÍN, HUILA.
SAN AGUSTÍN, REGIONAL
CLASSICAL PERIOD.
1 A.D. - 900 A.D.
O24251

OTHER CHIEFTAINSHIP SOCIETIES IN THE WORLD

According to archaeologists' classifications for the study of societies, chieftainships are societies that are not states yet which are ones where differences of rank exist between members of the social group. These differences may have their origin in social prestige, wealth, or the political or spiritual power exercised by certain members, and they are visible from the archaeological point of view in the rich funerary attire that was buried alongside the leaders. Many metallurgical societies in different parts of the world were organised along these lines, such as the one that erected the famous ceremonial stone circle at Stonehenge, in southern England, during the final European Neolithic Period. JSP

The river is a different world. It lives, breathes and moves.
The river has a memory. It tells stories of ancient times,
when fish were people and the ancestors walked along paths
that lead to the underworld. Those paths are our rivers.

MAKUNA MYTHOLOGY

Pendant in the form of a winged fish
3.1 X 9.7 CM
SAN AGUSTÍN, HUILA
SAN AGUSTÍN, REGIONAL CLASSICAL PERIOD
1 A.D. - 900 A.D.
032924

A Being of Water and Air

In the thought of many indigenous peoples, animals have skills that would be the envy of any human being, such as the strength, sharp eyesight or shrewdness that numerous species of birds, quadrupeds and lizards are said to have. From a profound knowledge of their environment, based on close observation of the habitat and behaviour of each animal, indian wise men build a world where animals are essentially people, and in them they see the apparel of people who are just like any one of them. Wildlife has been a constant source of inspiration for indigenous peoples ever since pre-Hispanic times, as thousands of objects which allude to beings whose importance we can barely guess at bear testimony to. With its slender, stylised figure, this winged fish, which was found in a tomb at San Agustín, is probably a synthesis of two worlds, air and water: the very essence of life. **J S P**

Upper Magdalena - Tierradentro

The Spaniards called the mountain knots and deep canyons in the north eastern part of Cauca province *"tierra adentro"*, or *"land within"*, because they felt they were cut off, or shut in, there by the high mountains. The rugged terrain on the spurs of the Central Cordillera and in a number of small and medium-sized valleys formed by rivers like the Ullucos, Páez, Moras and Negro does, in fact, give the visitor that impression. Two thirds of the area is a volcanic formation. Trees are scarce, although there are fruit trees in some places. Nowadays, the region is inhabited by Nasa or Páez indigenous groups, concentrated principally in the towns of Inzá, Belalcázar and Nátaga, where they grow corn, beans, coffee, onions, potatoes and marrows. From 1000 B.C. onwards and throughout the Early, Middle and Late periods, communities of farmers and potters lived there, and these have left us their funerary architecture, their statues and their metalwork. **J S P**

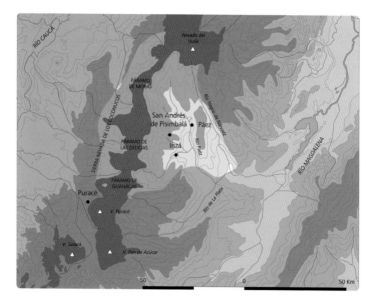

>
Avocado peak, in San Andrés de Pisimbalá,
Tierradentro

Anthropomorphous alcarraza
15.7 X 14.5 CM
PÁEZ, CAUCA
TIERRADENTRO, MIDDLE PERIOD.
150 B.C. - 900 A.D.
C06292

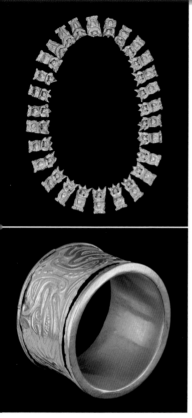

Necklace with zoomorphous beads
4 X 2.1 CM
PÁEZ, CAUCA
UPPER MAGDALENA, TIERRADENTRO.
O28922

Bracelet
5.4 X 8 CM
PÁEZ, CAUCA
TIERRADENTRO, MIDDLE PERIOD.
150 A.D. - 900 A.D.
O28443

Constructions for the Dead

The treatment given to the dead, together with every aspect of the funeral ritual, are practices that are closely linked to beliefs about the nature of death and the existence of another life after it. The ancient inhabitants of Tierradentro performed the funeral ritual twice. The body was first buried in direct shaft tombs with side chamber, along with offerings of pottery objects, items for grinding corn, necklaces and metal ornaments. Then, after a certain period of time, perhaps even years, a secondary burial was performed, which involved disinterring the remains and placing them in pottery urns or vessels, which were subsequently deposited in hypogea, or collective tombs. Excavated in soft volcanic rock on the mountain ridges, the hypogea are a typical feature of the Tierradentro region. Many of these funerary constructions are believed to date back to the Middle Period, between 150 B.C. and 900 A.D. Up to eight metres deep, access to them was by means of stairs carved out of the actual rock. The urns were deposited inside them, in an oval chamber with vaulted roof and lateral niches. These chambers were very often decorated as if they were homes, so this type of funerary architecture expresses ideas about life and society. **JSP**

**Breastplate with
zoomorphous figure**
33 X 26.3 CM
PÁEZ, CAUCA
TIERRADENTRO, MIDDLE
PERIOD.
150 A.D. - 900 A.D.
O24969

Vessel
9 X 13.5 CM
PÁEZ, CAUCA.
TIERRADENTRO, EARLY PERIOD.
1000 B.C. - 150 A.D.
C06291

**Alcarraza in the form
of a toad or frog**
15 X 16.3 CM
PÁEZ, CAUCA
TIERRADENTRO, MIDDLE PERIOD.
150 A.D. - 900 A.D.
C11067

Archaeological Parks, Heritage of Mankind

Funerary urn found in a hypogeum
25.3 X 38.5 CM
TIERRADENTRO, MIDDLE PERIOD
150 A.D. - 900 A.D.
C03072

The monumental expressions of the societies governed by chieftainships at San Agustín and Tierradentro are outstanding features of the Upper Magdalena region. To the incomparable natural beauty of this region must be added the attraction of the archaeological parks that are open to the public. In San Agustín Park, the burial mounds and the monumental stone statues typical of the Regional Classical Period can be visited. At Tierradentro, on the other hand, the monumental manifestations are not on the surface, but rather underground, and the visitor who has climbed the rugged mountains has to descend into the tombs or hypogea, with their smooth walls that are profusely decorated with red and black geometric designs on a white background. These were the last resting places of leading figures from this region. Also preserved at Tierradentro is the beautiful doctrinal chapel of San Andrés de Pisimbalá, built in 1785 to indoctrinate the Nasa indians who today live alongside the tombs, which they consider to be other people's. Both parks, which are run by the Colombian Institute of Anthropology and History, were declared to be part of the heritage of mankind by UNESCO in 1995. **JSP**

Statues and landscape, San Agustín Archaeological Park

Interior of a hypogeum decorated with painted geometric figures, in Tierradentro Archaeological Park

Mid-Magdalena Valley - Tolima

The burning hot banks of the River Magdalena and the slopes of the Central and Eastern Cordilleras have witnessed human settlement for more than 16,000 years, since the time when hunters and gatherers moved around the region, between grasslands and wooded areas. Subsequently, societies settled more permanently in different regions, engaging in activities like fishing, hunting and gathering. In Tolima and the northern part of Huila, archaeologists have recorded human settlements which left stone and pottery remains behind 3,000 years ago that expressed a tremendous cultural diversity. And at the time of the Conquest, the Spaniards were also surprised at the variety of farming groups, potters and metalsmiths that they encountered. **S M V**

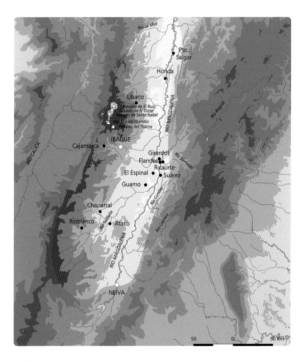

Valley of the River Magdalena between Tolima and Huila

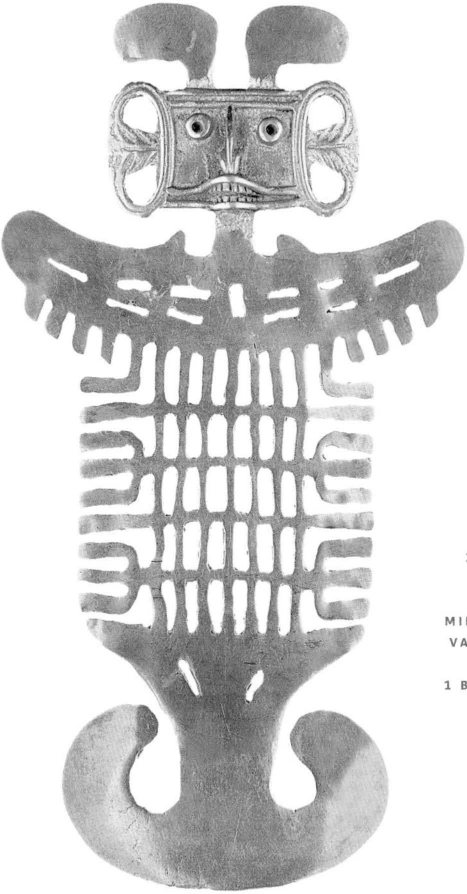

**Anthropo-
zoomorphous
breastplate**
16 X 8.7 CM
MID-MAGDALENA
VALLEY, MIDDLE
PERIOD
1 B.C. - 700 A.D.
O06418

Breastplate in the form of a jaguar
29 X 14.4 CM
CAMPOHERMOSO, ATACO,
TOLIMA.
MID-MAGDALENA VALLEY,
MIDDLE PERIOD.
1 B.C. - 700 A.D.
005832

Ancient Potters on the Banks of the Mid-Magdalena River

Pottery is the material culture that has been most studied by archaeologists in this vast region. Raw materials, forms, designs and finishes are but a few of the characteristics that have enabled similarities and differences to be established between the social groups that lived there.

Objects are dynamic social players, as they indicate uses, movements and appropriations. Thus, pottery depicts beliefs, values and transformations when it is found in burial areas or on housing sites, or when it suggests barter, power or blood relations because it appears in different areas. Archaeological research in the Mid-Magdalena region has enabled two different areas to be established, broadly speaking, as far as pottery production was concerned: the River Magdalena valley itself, and the eastern slopes of the Central Cordillera.

In one of these areas, the pots, plates, bowls and *alcarrazas* have incised decorations, appliqué work and small notches or crests. The beginnings of this tradition in the Mid-Magdalena valley date back right to the start of our era, while in central Tolima, where it is known as the Undulating Guamo Complex, it was used until the 8th century A.D.

Other human groups produced a markedly different pottery tradition, one to which archaeologists have given the name Montalvo Complex. This could date back as far as a thousand years before Christ, and it is noted for the profusion of goblets, three-legged decanters and pots, and fine decoration in which negative painting, geometric designs and graffito abound.

It should be stressed that despite similarities in the transformation of the landscape in this region, also in the economy based around fishing, agriculture and the hunting of the smaller wildlife species, and perhaps even in the ways in which life and death were viewed, a marked regionalism or individuality can be noted in the production of both pottery and metal objects. Although these latter

Globular vessel
11.7 X 17 CM
CHICORAL, ESPINAL,
TOLIMA.
MID-MAGDALENA VALLEY,
MIDDLE PERIOD.
1 B.C. - 700 A.D.
C13367

Alcarraza
16.3 X 18.5 CM
CHICORAL, ESPINAL,
TOLIMA.
MID-MAGDALENA
VALLEY,
MIDDLE PERIOD.
1 B.C. - 700 A.D.
C13372

Globular vessel
20.1 X 21 CM
LLANO PELAO,
ESPINAL, TOLIMA.
MID-MAGDALENA
VALLEY, EARLY
PERIOD.
1000 B.C. - 1 A.D.
C13410

are related to the technologies of Calima and the Mid-Cauca region, they display designs and iconographies that are all their own.

Other pottery has been dated as coming from between the 9th century and the time of the Spanish Conquest. Unlike the complexes mentioned, the decoration on this material is simpler, and there are important formal variations, such as the presence of handles, large bowls, and incised decoration around the edges and the upper parts of vessels. It was generally unpainted, and was used for domestic and funeral purposes. **SMV**

Goblet
25.8 X 16.1 CM
LLANO PELAO,
ESPINAL, TOLIMA.
MID-MAGDALENA
VALLEY, EARLY
PERIOD.
1000 B.C. - 1 A.D.
C13404

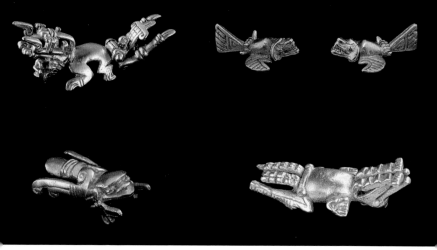

Schematised zoomorphous pendants

· 5,7 X 1,7 CM
CAMPOHERMOSO, ATACO, TOLIMA
MID-MAGDALENA VALLEY, MIDDLE PERIOD.
1 B.C. - 700 A.D.
O05871

· 4,3 X 2,2 CM   CHAPARRAL, TOLIMA
MID-MAGDALENA VALLEY,
MIDDLE PERIOD.
1 B.C. - 700 A.D.
O30427

· 3.8 X 2.2 CM · 3.9 X 2.2 CM
MID-MAGDALENA VALLEY,
MIDDLE PERIOD.
1 B.C. - 700 A.D.
O06514, O05871

· 4,3 X 1,8 CM   QUINDÍO
MID-MAGDALENA VALLEY,
MIDDLE PERIOD.
1 B.C. - 700 A.D.
O02921

FANTASTIC ANIMALS: MYTHICAL WILDLIFE ON THE HOT BANKS OF THE MAGDALENA

The mighty River Magdalena is home to a wide variety of wildlife. Small alligators, fish, birds and numerous insects stimulated the imagination of the people living on its banks, inspiring them to create representations in gold: fantastic animals, a mixture of carnivores, reptiles and winged fish, which recreate the prey and the hunter. **SMV**

**Schematised
zoomorphous pendant**
4.1 X 3.2 CM
VALLE DEL CAUCA
MID-MAGDALENA VALLEY,
MIDDLE PERIOD.
1 B.C. - 700 A.D.
O06400

Bats: another way of viewing the world.

People are accustomed to looking at the world with their feet firmly on the ground. Seeing it upside down therefore requires a major mental effort, one which totally alters our view of reality and the way we perceive things. Imagining sleeping, eating or procreating with your feet "on the roof" must have presented pre-Hispanic indigenous groups with a big challenge. The shamans and priests faced up to this, inspired by a small winged mammal, and ended up delving into a universe where reality was transformed.

This tiny being, the bat, has highly individual habits and powers, and these were depicted on breastplates and earring pendants made by Tolima craftsmen. Flapping wings made of fine membranes covered with skin, short neck, wide thorax, narrow abdomen, small eyes and big ears: these are just some of the characteristics that were stressed.

Bats are nocturnal creatures, and depending on the particular species, they feed on wild fruits (they help scatter the seeds), insects and arthropods (they control pests), pollen and nectar (pollinators), fish, amphibians, reptiles, small birds and mammals (carnivores), and blood (haematophagous). The anti-coagulant power of their saliva is the subject of research, as it can prevent thrombi, heart attacks or brain haemorrhages.

Carnivorous and fish- and insect-eating species abound in Tolima, and these inspired metalsmiths, who made pendants and necklace beads in their likeness. As pollinators and scatterers of seeds, they help regenerate woodland. Their skin, when covered with golden pollen, resembles the splendour of gold. **S M V**

<
Breastplate
19.7 X 8.7 CM
RIOBLANCO, TOLIMA.
MID-MAGDALENA VALLEY,
MIDDLE PERIOD.
1 B.C. - 700 A.D.
O06235

Earring pendants in the form of a bat
• 7.7 X 11.3 CM
• 7.5 X 11.9 CM
RIOBLANCO AND
CHAPARRAL, TOLIMA.
O05930 / O05913

• 7.1 X 10.7 CM
• 6.9 X 10.5 CM
CAMPOHERMOSO, ATACO,
TOLIMA.
MID-MAGDALENA VALLEY,
MIDDLE PERIOD.
1 B.C. - 700 A.D.
O05836 / O05837

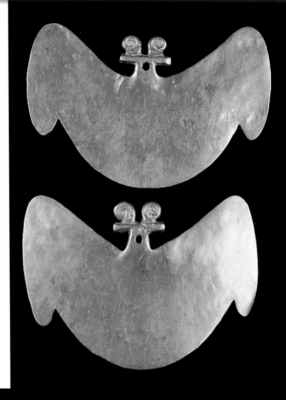

TOLIMA ICONS: HERITAGE AND ADVERTISING

Metalwork objects classified as being in Tolima style have become firm favourites in the minds of Colombians, as they have been reinvented and appropriated by the media to stress the legacy of an ancient tradition that has withstood the ravages of time. Because of their characteristic graphic, striking form, these objects have been reborn as logos for drinks, handicrafts, lotteries and fashion articles, where Colombia's goldworking heritage is seen as being another way of expressing identity. **SMV**

Life in the World of the Dead

Funeral architecture, body postures, the number of individual persons buried, and the funerary attire and offerings that were deposited in tombs are clear examples of the importance that was placed on death as another stage in life.

Some of the burial sites archaeologists have found are direct shaft tombs, where the corpse was placed on the ground. One such site was excavated in the town of Suárez, Tolima, and the funerary attire consisted of *alcarrazas* and globular vessels, a breastplate and a number of earring pendants made of gold, necklaces, and numerous shell beads. The pottery vessels show no signs of use, and appear to have been made specially to accompany the deceased.

Another form of burial, perhaps the most common, consisted of shaft tombs with one or two side chambers that were sealed off by stone slabs. These could

accommodate one or more individuals, or occasionally an adult with babies whose remains were deposited inside an urn. Profusely decorated pottery objects, mostly goblets with no signs of having been used, predominate in the funerary attire. The fact that ash is present in some tombs points to the bodies having been cremated before the urn was deposited.

Group of breastplates and pendants

Urn
68 X 33.8 CM
MID-MAGDALENA
VALLEY, LATE PERIOD.
1 B.C. - 700 A.D.
C00787

Funerary chair
35.6 X 20.4 CM
BARROSO, GUAMO,
TOLIMA.
MID-MAGDALENA
VALLEY, MIDDLE
PERIOD.
1 B.C. - 700 A.D.
C00848

Pottery seats of different sizes have also been found, decorated with schematised human figures and with snakes and frogs, recalling the transmutation of the skin. These were possibly made around the 4th century A.D.

By the 9th century A.D., and even after the Conquest, burial sites along the course of the River Magdalena were rectangular shaft tombs with various side chambers, in which the deceased were placed in urns that had lids. Anthropomorphous figures sitting on benches often decorate these lids, perhaps to refer to the hierarchical status of the deceased or to recall the passage to the world of the spirits when sacred beverages are drunk, which can be deduced from the vessels that some have in their hands. **S M V**

Funerary attire from a tomb excavated in the town of Suárez, Tolima.

Quindío
landscape with
wax palms,
*Xeroxylon
quindiuense*

Mid-Cauca – Quimbaya

The Mid-Cauca Region, consisting of the mountainous basin of the River Cauca in the present-day provinces of Quindío, Risaralda and Caldas, was inhabited for thousands of years by groups of people with different cultures and ways of life, who took full advantage of the great variety of climates and the abundant mineral, vegetation and wildlife resources. But these groups also had to cope with adverse conditions, such as volcanic eruptions and other phenomena that these triggered off.

The earliest inhabitants, ten thousand years ago, were hunters and gatherers. The region was then settled for several thousand years by groups who exploited the woodland and other ecosystems. Later, in the Early and Late Periods during the two thousand years before the Conquest, it was inhabited by farmers and gold and salt miners, and pottery and metalwork craftsmen, who with time came to develop social systems governed by rank and centralised power structures. Around 1540, the Europeans encountered a large, diverse population, which the wars of conquest then proceeded to decimate and displace. **MAU**

**Phytomorphous
lime container**
16.8 X 10.4 CM
MID-CAUCA,
EARLY PERIOD.
500 B.C. - 700 A.D.
O06074

Material Culture of the Early Period

Societies with a rich material culture inhabited Mid-Cauca and the Antioquia massif during the Early Period, and their pottery and metalwork are well known to us.

Pottery in the Brownware Incised style consisted of containers for domestic, economic and ritual activities. Although the different vessels were made for specific practices, such as drying salt or keeping the ashes of the deceased in, some were put to various uses during their long lives. Domestic pots and bowls have been found that were used in homes for keeping food in or eating it out of, and which were subsequently used as funerary urns or for covering urns. These containers have helped define social groups: some finely-worked urns recreated the high status of the deceased and his or her descendants, or could occasionally have been employed to raise a person's status.

Classical or Early Quimbaya metalwork consisted mainly of body ornaments and coca paraphernalia, in which, as with pottery, female forms and fruits predominated, with an emphasis on volume and shine. These artefacts were prestigious assets for leaders, and they played an essential role in their respective functions. **MAU**

Phytomorphous
bowl
7 X 1.8 CM
MID-CAUCA,
EARLY PERIOD.
500 B.C. - 700 A.D.
C00507

Helmet
11.2 X 19.1 CM
PUERTO NARE,
ANTIOQUIA.
MID-CAUCA,
EARLY PERIOD.
500 B.C. - 700 A.D.
C32933

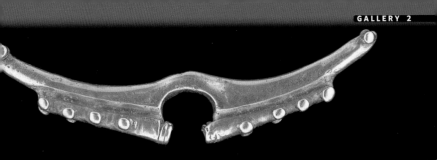

Nose ring
1.5 X 5.4 CM
MID-CAUCA, EARLY PERIOD.
500 B.C. - 700 A.D.
C01462

Phytomorphous funerary urn
17.6 X 13.7 CM
MID-CAUCA, EARLY PERIOD.
500 B.C. - 700 A.D.
C00499

**Lime container in the form
of a female figure**
24 X 11.8 CM
JAMARRAYA, PUEBLORRICO, RISARALDA.
MID-CAUCA, EARLY PERIOD.
400 B.C.
O00382

MATERIAL CULTURE

'Material' is frequently understood as referring to the tangible, inanimate, passive world that surrounds us, while 'culture' is associated with customs, rituals, values and institutions. But this differentiation is inadequate because, as various recent theoretical currents emphasize, artefacts play an active role in constructing and transforming identities, relations and social institutions; materiality is an essential and necessary component of them. **MAU**

Two Exceptional Early Funerary Attires

A group of outstanding pottery and metalwork objects from the Early Period was found in 1890 in two tombs in Soledad, which comes under the town of Filandia, in Quindío. Referred to as the *Treasure of the Quimbayas* by academics of the day, who attributed it to this 16th century *provincia*, most of its gold objects were acquired by the Colombian government so they could represent the country at the 1892 exposition in Madrid to commemorate the four hundredth anniversary of the discovery of America. After the event, they were donated to the Spanish crown, and are today on display in the Museum of America in Madrid.

The group consisted of almost two hundred metal artefacts and an unknown quantity of pottery objects. The former included ornaments such as helmets, nose rings, earrings and necklaces, and containers and sticks that were used when coca leaves were being chewed. Such rich funerary attires as these could have belonged to political - religious leaders in the 3rd century A.D., according to a date obtained from a pendant ornament.

Funerary attire found at Puerto Nare, Antioquia
MID-CAUCA, EARLY PERIOD
500 B.C. - 700 A.D.

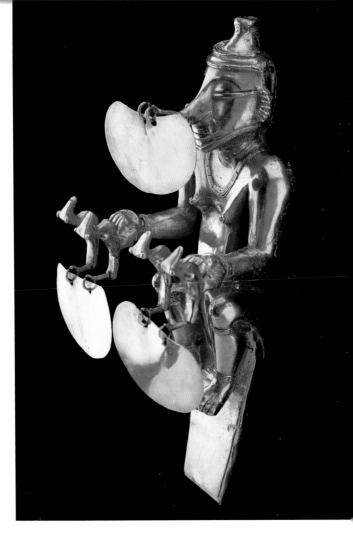

**Lime container
in the form of
a female figure**
27.1 X 11.8 CM
PUERTO NARE,
ANTIOQUIA
MID-CAUCA,
EARLY PERIOD
500 B.C. -
700 A.D.
O32852

The Gold Museum has a funerary attire amongst its collections that was
found a century later in Puerto Nare, in the Mid-Magdalena region of Antioquia,
which is very much like the Treasure of the Quimbayas in both content and style.
Consisting of fifteen metalwork objects, including helmets, crowns, container
necks and containers, it shares with the Treasure a certain sober style, female and
fruit forms, tumbaga of different colours, and the casting technique. But there are
differences, as well: ornaments are scarce amongst the Museum's artefacts, and
there are no lime sticks, which are common features of the Treasure. **MAU**

>
Phytomorphous lime container
29.3 X 13.4 CM
PUERTO NARE, ANTIOQUIA.
MID-CAUCA, EARLY PERIOD.
500 B.C. - 700 A.D.
032857

Phytomorphous lime container
11 X 9.5 CM
FILANDIA, QUINDÍO
MID-CAUCA, EARLY PERIOD.
500 B.C. - 700 A.D.
O00338

Vegetable Forms

Humans and animals are depicted frequently in Colombian archaeological materials, but images of flora are scarce. The material culture of the Early Period is one of the few where these forms abound. They appear on pottery and metal containers which imitate pumpkins, marrows and gourds, *Lagenaria siceraria* fruits and other climbing plants of the same family, and also on containers that copy gourds, the fruit of the calabash tree or *Crescentia cujete*. All these fruits have been used in America since time immemorial for making countless artefacts, such as containers, utensils, masks, maracas and floats. **MAU**

Phytomorphous funerary urn
20.5 X 40 CM
GUASABRA,
ANTIOQUIA.
MID-CAUCA,
EARLY PERIOD.
500 B.C. - 700
A.D.
C13360

WHY WOMEN AND PUMPKINS?

Women and pumpkins, marrows and gourds: these are two of the principal recurring themes in Early Period material culture. They appear on the same types of artefact, such as pottery funerary urns and gold *poporos*, and are sometimes combined on a single object. Some type of identification appears to have existed between women and these fruits, and in the light of ethnography, this is highly likely. Many American indigenous peoples and similar groups on other continents associate women with pots, baskets, shoulder bags and other containers, since all of them are thought to hold substances that are vital for the group to reproduce, and inside them these substances undergo major transformations: they develop, combine, cook and ferment. **MAU**

Funerary urn in the shape of a hunched female figure
18 X 14 CM
GUASABRA, ANTIOQUIA.
MID-CAUCA, EARLY PERIOD.
500 B.C. - 700 A.D.
C13350

Phytomorphous funerary urn
28.2 X 22 CM
MONTENEGRO, QUINDÍO
MID-CAUCA, EARLY PERIOD.
500 B.C. - 700 A.D.
C00711

Male anthropomorphous figure
25.8 X 21 CM
MID-CAUCA, LATE PERIOD.
700 A.D. - 1600 A.D.
C04542

Body Paint and other Body Art

Human figures and artefacts for bodily use from Mid-Cauca have enabled archaeologists to investigate the cultural dimension that the body enjoyed in this region in the past. Paint is one of the best-documented customs. A wide range of red designs was used in the Early Period, and one where two lines cross the face longitudinally, passing through the centre of the eyes, is particularly outstanding. Curved drawings with interlaced spirals were painted on the body, and these motifs can also be seen in the decoration of objects. Ligatures were also tied to the arms and legs, the teeth were filed, and the higher-ranking figures wore metal ornaments.

These customs changed in the Late Period, and new ones appeared. Deformation of the skull was introduced, and rollers and stamps to print designs on the skin became popular. Warriors and chieftains sometimes painted their whole body with annatto (*Bixa orellana*); unlike the previous period, more people were able to adorn their bodies with metal objects. **MAU**

Pendant
3 X 2.6 CM
SAN MIGUEL, SONSÓN, ANTIOQUIA
MID-CAUCA, EARLY PERIOD.
500 B.C. - 700 A.D.
O32805

Nose ring with spiral fretwork
1 X 2.1 CM
MID-CAUCA, EARLY PERIOD.
500 B.C. - 700 A.D.
004003

THE BODY IN CONTEXT

Recent theory has questioned the principal dichotomies that exist in the western world and which have influenced the very foundations of the social sciences, such as nature / culture, individual / society, and body / mind. These new perspectives criticise the way the west depicts the body as a universal biological entity on which culture is superimposed, and view it today rather as a historical, cultural and social product that can only be understood in context. The body is as much a product of society and culture as it is an active agent that creates and transforms society and culture. In virtually all societies, the ways in which people adorn, move and imagine their bodies have, for example, been key elements in the construction of gender, ethnic, family and rank identities. **MAU**

Female anthropomorphous pendant
10.1 X 6.1 CM
MID-CAUCA, EARLY PERIOD.
500 B.C. - 700 A.D.
066416

Relations with Animals

Archaeological and ethno-historical evidence has revealed details of the role that animals played in the ancient societies of the Mid-Cauca Region. In the Early Period, people settled near streams and wetlands, where they caught birds, fish and other wildlife. A range of different animal icons was depicted in their metalwork, notably chrysalises, grasshopper pupas and other insects in a state of metamorphosis, and small land and sea snails, which were often portrayed in pairs. These species undoubtedly had a special, symbolic importance.

The conquistadors marvelled at the lush forests and vast expanses of *guadua* (bamboo) in the region. The chroniclers tell of how in the different "*provincias*", people hunted deer, peccaries, foxes, pacas, armadillos and rabbits; they also say that people fished, gathered honey, and bred guinea pigs in their homes, along with animals the Spaniards called "silent dogs". The fact that beads made from dogs' teeth have been found in tombs suggests that this animal also had symbolic connotations attached to it. Frogs and lizards predominate in artefacts from the Late Period, and jaguar-man, frog-man and lizard-man figures appear, images that are perhaps related to the chieftains who, we are told, wore body paint, loincloths with a "tail" and long nails, to make them look like the "big cats" that they saw in their trances. **MAU**

> Pendant in
the form of an
insect cocoon
10 X 6.4 CM
CORINTO, CAUCA.
MID-CAUCA,
EARLY PERIOD.
500 B.C. - 700 A.D.
O00089

Pendant in the form of a double land snail
2.7 X 4.9 CM
MID-CAUCA, EARLY PERIOD.
500 B.C. - 700 A.D.
O00095

Breastplate with anthropo-zoomorphous figure
17.5 CM
MONTENEGRO,
QUINDÍO
MID-CAUCA,
LATE PERIOD.
700 A.D. - 1600 A.D.
O04688

Pendant in the form of a sea snail
13.7 X 2 CM
MID-CAUCA,
EARLY PERIOD.
500 B.C. - 700 A.D.
O06035

Pendant in the form of a lizard
13.6 X 3.5 CM
QUINDÍO
MID-CAUCA, LATE PERIOD.
970 A.D.
O06518

Nose ring with
spirals and birds
7.3 X 16.4 CM
ARMENIA, QUINDÍO
MID-CAUCA, LATE PERIOD.
700 A.D. - 1600 A.D.
O02347

Diversity in Later Times

Alongside a notable growth in the population, a number of cultural diversification and complex social processes occurred during the Late Period in the Mid-Cauca region. Evidence points to there having been numerous different societies, with countless social divisions between them, and to these having undergone major transformations as time progressed. The chronicles tell of a vast group of "*provincias*" or chieftainships, with differences of language, customs and socio-political organisation: those of the Ansermas, Quindos, Armas, Quimbayas and others, who are still recalled today in place names around the region.

Late Period material culture is very varied, with countless individual, local peculiarities, in marked contrast to the previous Period. In pottery, differences exist between the materials used in the north, with rhomboidal shapes and appliqué and incised decorations, and those in the south, where negative paint, conical shapes and human figurines are common. A further notable feature is that more metalwork was produced in the south, where numerous circular breastplates, flat and plaited nose rings, sub-labial ornaments and appliqué work for the skin, some made using innovative technologies, have been found.

MAU

Amphora with
anthropomorphous face
35.3 X 30.8 CM
MID-CAUCA, LATE PERIOD.
700 A.D. - 1600 A.D.
C02446

THE NEW TASTE FOR COPPER

Archaeological digs in Late Period Mid-Cauca tombs have recently revealed numerous ornaments made of copper: annular, half-moon shaped and plaited nose rings, heart-shaped breastplates, and necklace beads. We do not know why the metalsmiths chose this particular material for making those objects, but several contexts suggest that like gold, copper was also thought to be very valuable. A deep shaft tomb that was excavated at La Tebaida had two chambers, and each one contained a body wrapped in a bundle and embellished with a copper breastplate. One of the bodies had been covered with two different layers of earth, and had other ornaments made of the same metal. **MAU**

Heart-shaped copper breastplate
19.9 X 25.5 CM
MONTENEGRO, QUINDÍO
MID-CAUCA, LATE PERIOD.
700 A.D. - 1600 A.D.
O15411

Rhomboid -shaped anthropo- morphous vessel with frogs
19.5 X 25.5 CM
APÍA, RISARALDA
MID-CAUCA,
LATE PERIOD.
700 A.D.
- 1600 A.D.
C13353

Upper Cauca - Cauca

Metalwork in the Cauca or Popayán style comes from the Popayán valley region and surrounding areas, and from both slopes of the Central Cordillera in Cauca. Evidence has led archaeologists to believe that it was made in later periods, around the time of the Conquest, perhaps by Pubenenses or peoples from Guambía, Jabaló, Caloto and other places, who are referred to in the chronicles as being agricultural groups who settled in villages or were scattered around the valleys and on the mountain slopes, and were governed by chieftains of differing ranks. MAU

Pendant in the form of
a two-headed bird
14.5 X 7.7 CM
INZÁ, CAUCA.
UPPER CAUCA, LATE PERIOD.
900 A.D. - 1600 A.D.
O29704

>
Silvia
mountains
in the Upper
Cauca region

Transformation Iconography

Cauca style is notable for its iconography, for its hybrid beings in which human, bird, quadruped and frog elements are combined. Breastplates and pendants in the form of a bird-man are common, where the hooked beak and wide, spread wings and tail suggest birds of prey. Another frequently-encountered figure is a small quadruped with coiled tail and bird's head, placed all alone on a stick or accompanied by bird-men. Frog-men, bird-frogs and bird-frog-men are also known. A notable feature of many images is the use of a plaited nose ring with large head in the form of a disk; this was a common metal ornament which probably helped transform the identity of whoever wore it. It is difficult to know what the precise meanings were of these images, but they seem to have referred to the transformation of the shaman into a bird, to the flight of the shaman, and to the continuity between man and animals. **MAU**

Breastplate in the form of a frog-bird-man
15.8 X 12.8 CM
LOS ROBLES, JAMUNDÍ, VALLE DEL CAUCA.
UPPER CAUCA, LATE PERIOD.
900 A.D. - 1600 A.D.
O33481

Breastplate in the form of a bird-man
24 X 16.5 CM
PUEBLILLO, POPAYÁN, CAUCA.
UPPER CAUCA, LATE PERIOD.
900 A.D. - 1600 A.D.
O03038

Lime stick with head in the form of a bird-quadruped
7.4 X 1.5 CM
QUINDÍO
UPPER CAUCA, LATE PERIOD.
900 A.D. - 1600 A.D.
O03106

THE LA MARQUESA CONTEXT

When defining Cauca metalwork, researchers have based themselves on stylistic criteria, and on a small number of known associations, such as the La Marquesa funerary attire that was discovered around 1930 in Timbío, Cauca. Although it was found by tomb raiders, it was documented by the archaeologists of the day.

The tomb was of the shaft type with a side chamber, and in this chamber were buried an individual, together with a group of outstanding artefacts. A large metal breastplate in the shape of a bird-man with feathered headdress and spread tail had been placed on the body of the deceased; a necklace of frogs, a nose ring, a stick cover and a bird completed his attire. Additionally, there were various male pottery figures seated on benches with a fantastic animal on the back, seemingly warriors in view of the shield they were holding. **MAU**

Caribbean Plains - Zenú Tradition

The Caribbean Plains in northern Colombia have been inhabited by numerous different societies for around 11,000 years. The rich and varied environments were exploited initially by groups of hunters and gatherers, and then later by societies of farmers, potters and metalworkers. About 6,000 years ago, communities on the San Jacinto Range made some of the first pottery in America.

From around 200 B.C., this marshy region progressively came to be inhabited by farming and metalworking groups who, with the passing of time, formed Zenú societies. They had a unique way of relating to their environment, and shared the same concepts about life and death. Farmers, fishermen, traders, metalworkers and weavers were organised in groups that were ruled over by local lords, who in turn paid tribute to three regional chieftains: Finzenú, who ruled along the River Sinú, Panzenú, the leader on the floodable plains of the River San Jorge, and the mythical chieftain Zenufana in the lower River Cauca region, where gold deposits were exploited. Each region had complementary political, religious and economic functions.

In the floodable area, the Zenúes built an extensive waterway system, which

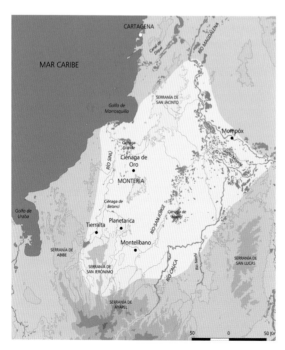

was used for more than 1300 years to drain off floodwater so it could be put to good purpose. In the 16th century, they still built burial mounds and made metal ornaments and pottery objects just as their ancestors had done, perpetuating a long cultural tradition that has continued down to the present day. By that time, however, they shared the

Caribbean Plains. San Marcos, Sucre

Anthropomorphous pendant
7 X 9.6 CM   SAN MARCOS, SUCRE.
CARIBBEAN PLAINS, ZENÚ TRADITION.
200 B.C. - 1600 A.D.
006403

territory with indigenous groups from the San Jacinto Range and the banks of the River Magdalena. It was this mixture of indigenous, white and negro communities that gave rise to the ethnic richness that is so typical of Colombia's Caribbean Plains. **JSS**

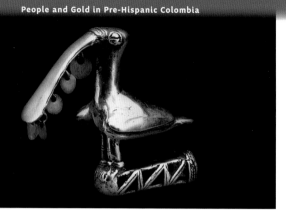

Staff finial
8.9 X 10.6 CM
CARIBBEAN PLAINS,
ZENÚ TRADITION
200 B.C. - 1600
A.D.
006444

Biodiversity Secrets

The marshes, rivers and grasslands of the Caribbean Plains were home to a rich and varied wildlife, which the Zenúes exploited to the full for their food. The different species were also religious and political symbols, and were thus depicted in their metalwork and pottery, and in bone, stone and shell carvings.

Remains have been found near pre-Hispanic homes of deer, great anteaters, rabbits, squirrels and armadillos, and - along with weights for fishing nets - the bones of fish such as bream and catfish. Giant tortoise and turtle shells and bones are likewise abundant, because their meat, skin, eggs and fat have always been traded and eaten in this region.

Feline figures and caimans were also incorporated into their political and religious leaders' symbols of power, and these were designed very realistically on breastplates, staff finials and pendants, or on pottery vessels that were used in rituals.

Curiously, the insects and snakes that abounded were not depicted so emphatically, and bats definitely played no part in this iconographic world. **JSS**

Staff finial
4.7 X 7.2 CM
SUCRE, SUCRE
CARIBBEAN PLAINS,
ZENÚ TRADITION. 1 A.D.
029226

THE GOLD CAIMAN

The caiman (*Crocodylus acutus*) held a particular symbolic relevance for the Zenúes. It is encountered on gold staff finials and breastplates, on pendants made from shells, and as decoration on pottery flutes. For the present-day Zenúes, who are descendants of the waterway system builders, the caiman is one of the principal features of their religious thought: the gold caiman, the subterranean spirit which supports the world and watches over the wellbeing of mankind, has the same dimensions as the territory that makes up the indigenous people's reserve, and they fear that if it were to be captured, it would mean the end of the world. The saurian also represents a physical support for the home, so much so that the central roof beam bears its name. The area occupied by the house is thus an inversion of the underground world inhabited by the great gold caiman. **JSS**

Flute in the form of a fish modelled in clay
29 X 6.5 CM
OVEJAS, SUCRE.
CARIBBEAN PLAINS, LATE ZENÚ
1000 A.D. - 1600 A.D.
C13389

Staff finial
4.5 X 10.9 CM
SAN MARCOS, SUCRE
CARIBBEAN PLAINS,
ZENÚ TRADITION
200 B.C. - 1600 A.D.
O06405

The Floodable Caribbean Plains

Every year, the Mompox Depression in the middle of the Caribbean Plains receives the waters of the rivers Magdalena, Cauca and San Jorge that flow down from the cordilleras. These floodwaters, which bring with them a fertile deposit of sediments, leave the area under water for eight months of the year. Nowadays, people suffer the loss of their homes and belongings, their crops and their cattle, year in year out, but in pre-Hispanic times, the Zenúes made the most of the water and silt. In a long process which was at its peak between 200 B.C. and 1000 A.D., they transformed the landscape by means of an ingenious water control system.

Man-made islands, on which ancient Zenúes used to build their houses

Long canals in the Carate stream, San Marcos, Sucre

The waterway system, consisting of an enormous network of canals and ridges, eventually covered an area of 500,000 hectares in the San Jorge basin, and a further 150,000 around the River Sinú.

The system set out to ensure that the courses of the rivers and channels remained stable. They were surrounded by artificial islets, on which people's homes were built. Perpendicular to these channels, the Zenúes dug canals ten metres apart and up to four kilometres long, along which the floodwater flowed to the marshes lower down. There, the

current was halted by means of short, interlinked canals between 30 and 70 metres long, so that large areas where crops were grown could be created.

This way, up to 2,000 hectares were made available for agriculture, as when the water levels dropped, the canals retained humidity throughout the dry season. The nutrient-rich sediments were gathered from the canal beds and taken to the tops of the raised fields to act as fertiliser, so that crops could be planted. Some sectors were dedicated to a single crop, while in

La Cruz marsh.
San Marcos,
Sucre

others various species were grown: coca (*Erythroxylum sp.*), corn (*Zea mays*), sweet potato (*Ipomoea batata*), pumpkin (*Cucurbita maxima*), chili (*Capiscum sp.*), marrow (*Cucurbita mixta*), cassava (*Manihot esculenta*) and many different fruits.

A strict, complex social and political organisation meant that the Zenúes were able to adapt the landscape and to keep the canals clean for an unbroken period of 1,300 years, thus enabling a large population to be fed without harming the environment. **JSS**

The Fertile Life Cycle

Zenú funeral ceremonies could be construed as having been a ritual where the concepts of life and death were related to the earth as the source of life, to which a person returned when he or she died. This is what is suggested from information that was gathered by the scribes and monks who visited the Caribbean Plains from the 16th century onwards, from archaeological evidence, and from the funeral practices of the Zenú communities that live in the San Andrés de Sotavento reserve today. Ever since life was first commemorated, rituals involved music, chanting and stories, in order to celebrate the deceased's journey to the underworld of gold, and they were occasions for bringing the community together, to restate its identity and to reinforce the prestige of the leaders.

The deceased was buried with his belongings, and generally alongside pregnant women moulded in clay. A mound was built over his grave, and a tree was planted on this. The tree and the roundness of the burial mound and of the clay women all appear to be symbols of fertility and the new life.

Periods of flooding and drought, abundant harvests, and the society itself reproducing, could all be related to women. Hence the religious and political importance of women in the 16th century, when the great religious centre in the *provincia* of Finzenú was ruled over by a female chieftain. **JSS**

Nose ring
2.2 X 13.8 CM
CARIBBEAN PLAINS,
ZENÚ TRADITION.
200 B.C. - 1600 A.D.
033684

THE WAY WOMEN WEAR THEIR CLOTHES

Around 1623, the historian Friar Pedro Simón commented that Zenú women *".....wear a blanket in the form of a cotton mantilla that is tied round the waist and extends down to the feet, sometimes painted and sometimes white, depending on the individual taste of each one.....".* Some women depicted in clay have drawings stamped on their chest, with designs that are similar to those on the woven blankets, and they are wearing earrings and necklaces just like the gold or shell ones found in the tombs. Others, naked and almost always pregnant, and with their knees bent as if they were about to give birth, are wearing nose rings, earrings, necklaces, breastplates and bracelets typical of the region. **JSS**

Breast-shaped breastplate
20.5 X 27 CM
SAN PEDRO DE URABÁ,
ANTIOQUIA
CARIBBEAN PLAINS,
ZENÚ TRADITION.
200 B.C. - 1600 A.D.
O31829

<
Female figure
12 X 17.5 CM
CARIBBEAN PLAINS,
ZENÚ TRADITION.
200 B.C. - 1600 A.D.
C12766

Goblet
30.2 X 19.5 CM
MONTERÍA, CÓRDOBA
CARIBBEAN PLAINS,
ZENÚ TRADITION.
200 B.C. - 1600 A.D.
C12857

The Weave Metaphor

Fabrics and the weave played an essential role in the daily and religious life of the Zenúes. In the 16th century, the Europeans praised the peoples along the River Sinú for the craftsmanship that was displayed in their blankets and hammocks, which were used in their temples for collecting offerings in.

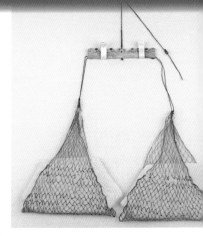

The weaving and basketwork industries influenced even pottery and metalwork styles. Metalsmiths used the cast filigree technique to make earrings, by weaving or imitating fabrics and plaits in wax threads, which they later transformed into metal. With filigree, they simulated the hair of mammals and birds' feathers. Potters produced real clay baskets adorned with fringes and animal figures, they modelled vessels which looked like simple baskets, either alone or standing on benches, and they went to great pains decorating women's skirts.

But more than that, the Zenúes lived amidst a maze of streams, rivers and marshes, and wove together a waterway system made up of an intricate network of canals. The numerous villages were linked together in an orderly weave of commercial, political and religious relationships, to form the vast Greater Zenú tapestry. The universe seems to have been an enormous filigree weave, on which men and wildlife lived together in a harmonious balance. **JSS**

Filigree earring
5.4 X 10.3 CM
CARIBBEAN PLAINS,
ZENÚ
TRADITION.
200 B.C. - 1600 A.D.
O04295

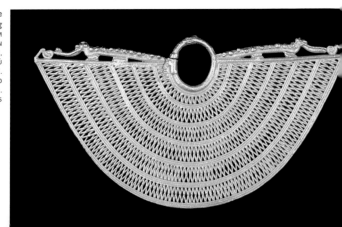

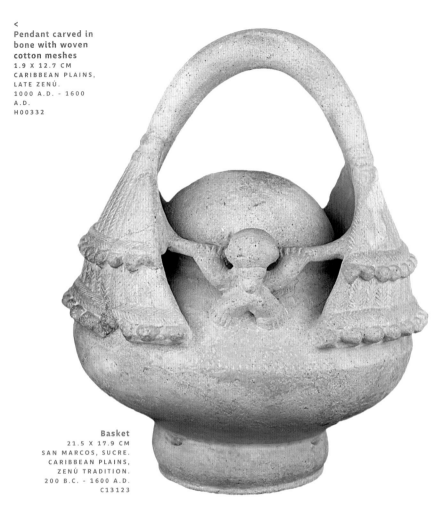

<
Pendant carved in bone with woven cotton meshes
1.9 X 12.7 CM
CARIBBEAN PLAINS,
LATE ZENÚ.
1000 A.D. – 1600 A.D.
H00332

Basket
21.5 X 17.9 CM
SAN MARCOS, SUCRE.
CARIBBEAN PLAINS,
ZENÚ TRADITION.
200 B.C. - 1600 A.D.
C13123

Filigree earring
5.2 X 8.7 CM
CARIBBEAN PLAINS,
ZENÚ TRADITION.
200 B.C. - 1600 A.D.
O10608

Peoples of the Plains, the Range and the River in the 16th Century

Around the year 1200 A.D., the Zenú population began to decline. Many groups retreated to the banks of the River Sinú and the high grasslands bordering the marshy zones, and part of their territory was settled by people who came from the River Magdalena. There and on the San Jacinto Range, evidence exists of other sailors, metalworkers and farmers, who took advantage of the floodwater in the river to fertilise their crops. They were related to the Zenúes and shared social relations and even religious ideas with them, and there were common themes in their metalwork, pottery and textiles. In the 16th century, the Spaniards called these peoples Malibúes.

Pendant
10.7 X 8.6 CM
PUERTO
ESCONDIDO,
CÓRDOBA.
CARIBBEAN
PLAINS,
LATE ZENÚ.
1000 A.D. –
1600 A.D.
071132

Despite the clear similarities with the Zenúes on the Plains, the peoples from the Range and the river were different, because they used copper-rich alloys to make metal ornaments depicting scenes in which amphibians, feline figures, birds and schematised human beings predominated. Their human figures, decked out with headdresses, sticks indicating their authority and ornaments on the chest, depicted important dignitaries showing off all the attributes of power. Also characteristic of their symbolic and iconographic thought are pendants with a human face and feathered headdress, which have extended bodies that could be a fish, a lizard or a crustacean, aquatic and mythical beings typical of those marshy and riverside environments.

Anthropo-
zoomorphous
pendant
9.2 X 6.8 CM
COLOSÓ, SUCRE
CARIBBEAN PLAINS,
LATE ZENÚ.
1000 A.D. -
1600 A.D.
O21333

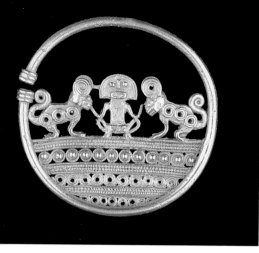

Earring
5.2 X 5.5 CM
COLOSÓ, SUCRE
CARIBBEAN PLAINS, LATE ZENÚ.
1000 A.D. - 1600 A.D.
019963

As with the Zenúes on the Plains, textiles and music were prominent features of their customs and their religious life. The Spaniards mention pipes, flutes, and pottery rattles or ones made from marrows. In 1589, Bartolomé Briones de Pedraza described a ceremony he attended in the lower Magdalena region in the following terms: "....*some wear a sort of feathered hat on their head..... all sitting in order on dúhos, which are the seats they use..... At the front of all of them are the leading figures..... and these leaders always have two gourds of chicha put in their hands..... and they have pipers who play very long flutes*".

Those who took part in these ceremonies can be seen on small copper or tumbaga staff finials. They are wearing woven diadems, earrings, nose rings and hats, and are carrying gourds and musical instruments. **JSS**

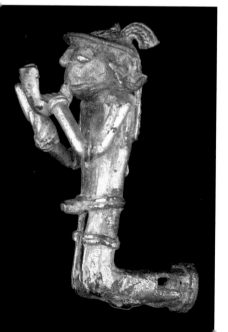

Staff finial
5,1 X 2,3 CM
ANTIOQUIA
CARIBBEAN PLAINS, LATE ZENÚ.
1000 A.D. - 1600 A.D.
033613

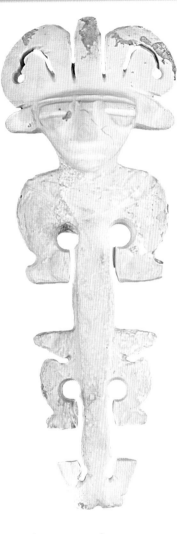

Staff finials
· 5,7 X 4,8 CM
· 5,8 X 3,5 CM
SUCRE, SUCRE.
CARIBBEAN PLAINS, LATE ZENÚ.
1000 A.D. - 1600 A.D.
023848 /O29805

**Anthropo-zoomorphous
pendant carved from shell**
12.3 X 4.6 CM
CARMEN DE BOLÍVAR, BOLÍVAR.
CARIBBEAN PLAINS, LATE ZENÚ.
1000 A.D. - 1600 A.D.
K00438

The Sierra Nevada de Santa Marta - Tairona

The Tairos or Taironas were but one of the groups that were living on the Sierra Nevada de Santa Marta in northern Colombia at the time of the Spanish Conquest. In the 17th century, however, the historian Lucas Fernández de Piedrahita referred to this *provincia* as ".....*the great nation of the Taironas*", and ever since then, that name has been the popular way to identify all traces of human habitation in the region, even if they relate to other people and other times.

Around 1000 B.C., small groups of farmers lived in the area around the Sierra, but it was not until 200 A.D. that villages appeared on the coast that were inhabited by potters, metalsmiths, farmers, fishermen and salt miners, who are identified in archaeological terms as the people from the Nahuange Period. With time, these

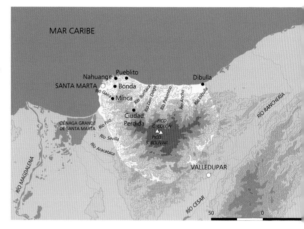

peoples spread up the slopes of the Sierra to the higher regions, and exploited the resources that were available from sea level right up to the perpetual snows. After 900 A.D., in the Tairona Period, the large population on the northern slopes of the Sierra appears to have been ruled over by powerful political and religious leaders, and to have lived in cities and villages built on stone foundations that were linked by paths, along which innumerable products moved back and forth. These were the Chibcha-speaking societies who did not succumb to the Spanish Conquest for 75 years.

When the Europeans succeeded in cutting off the barter networks, many indigenous peoples retreated to the highest and most inaccessible parts of the Sierra, to set up and live in new societies. This territory is currently inhabited by Koguis, Wiwas, Ikas and Kankuamos, who live in reserves that are ruled over by indigenous governors. **JSS**

Anthropo-zoomorphous breastplate
7.6 X 7.6 CM
SIERRA NEVADA
DE SANTA MARTA,
TAIRONA PERIOD.
900 A.D. - 1600 A.D.
O23822

Platforms and terraces along the central axis of the Lost City

Female pendant
6 X 3 CM
SANTA MARTA,
MAGDALENA
SIERRA NEVADA
DE SANTA MARTA,
NAHUANGE PERIOD.
200 A.D. - 900 A.D.
O15603

People during the Nahuange Period

By around 200 A.D., there were small villages of metalsmiths, farmers and fishermen along the bays and on the northern and western slopes of the Sierra Nevada de Santa Marta. From out at sea and from nearby beaches, marshes, mangrove swamps, rivers and hills, they obtained a wide variety of resources to complement their diet based on corn and other crops they grew. While the agricultural potential of some bays was great, others offered fishing possibilities on a large scale, and in yet others, where the water was shallow, salt deposits could be exploited.

**Pottery offering
container**
16.5 X 20.2 CM
SIERRA NEVADA DE SANTA
MARTA,
NAHUANGE PERIOD.
200 A.D. - 900 A.D.
C05858

Funeral practices suggest the existence of social ranks. Simple burials at the time of death have been noted; on some occasions there was a second phase, when the remains were disinterred and then buried once more in a special pottery ossuary or other vessel. Funerary offerings have been found in both cases, varying in terms of quantity and type of items deposited: objects in everyday use, or less frequently, numerous, diverse offerings, with much time and manpower having been spent on building a burial mound over the grave.

One feature of the stonework art of this period was the carving of jadeite. Pendants made of this material were common. There are numerous holes in them, some with clear signs of wear and tear from frequent use, and these enabled the pendants to be hung either vertically or horizontally. Pendants with female figures on them are exceptional.

Metallurgical production dates back to at least the first century A.D., when metalsmiths

Female pendant carved from jadeite
20.5 X 6.2 CM
SIERRA NEVADA DE SANTA
MARTA, NAHUANGE PERIOD.
200 A.D. - 900 A.D.
L03121

Diorama
AN ALLUSION TO THE TOMB FOUND IN 1922 ON NAHUANGE BAY

had a detailed knowledge of the properties of metals. Hammered artefacts predominated during the Nahuange Period, and to a lesser extent, objects made by pouring cast metal into clay moulds. These metalsmiths preferred copper and gold alloys (tumbaga), or to use copper that was virtually pure. Ornaments are typically thin, with a highly-polished, reddish visible surface, and the back yellow and opaque. The interest in polished, reddish surfaces could be related to very specific social, political or religious codes in the society. **JSS**

Pendant in the form of a frigate bird
3.5 X 8.4 CM
SANTA MARTA,
MAGDALENA
SIERRA NEVADA
DE SANTA MARTA,
NAHUANGE PERIOD.
480 A.D.
O16387

128

THE NAHUANGE TOMB AND THE IMPORTANCE OF ARCHAEOLOGY

In 1922, the American archaeologist John Alden Mason made the first scientific digs on the Sierra Nevada de Santa Marta. He dug various mounds on Nahuange Bay, and under one of them he found a vault that had been built with carefully-aligned stone slabs to form an irregular rectangle about two metres square. Inside were around twenty pottery vessels, tumbaga ornaments, and thousands of beads and carvings made from semi-precious stones. Since the human bones had decomposed due to the moisture in the soil, it is hard to say exactly how many persons were once buried in this grave. The funerary attire enabled the ornaments and objects that were worn by these peoples' leading dignitaries to be determined, and Mason already considered them to be somewhat different from the groups who lived there at the time of the Conquest, and from different eras. Then, in the late eighties, the clay and carbon core of a metal female figure found in the Nahuange tomb was radiocarbon dated as coming from 310 A.D. This date, and others obtained from new archaeological research along the coast, have confirmed how long the Period lasted, and it is currently defined as having been from 200 A.D. to 900 A.D. **JSS**

Breastplate
9.7 X 21.3 CM
SANTA MARTA, MAGDALENA
SIERRA NEVADA DE SANTA MARTA,
NAHUANGE PERIOD.
200 A.D. - 900 A.D.
O16129

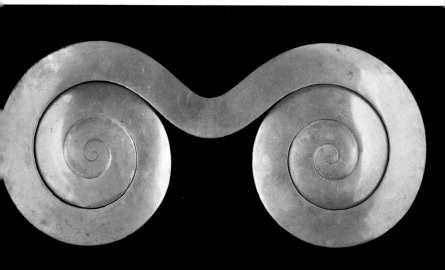

The Golden Eagles

Eagles were depicted on the Sierra Nevada de Santa Marta from the very earliest days of metalwork production, and the practice continued well into the Colonial era. Their symbolic and social importance to the pre-Hispanic peoples of the Sierra throughout this period is clear.

Nahuange Period metalsmiths made such diverse eagles that each one appears to be unique; they were generally very large. Some were simple and sober, while others had two or three heads and waists that were adorned with secondary birds or strips of triangles that seemingly depict the bodies of snakes. Some were cast, others hammered.

The figures portrayed became standardised and far more numerous after 1000 A.D. The number of central heads rose, some were decorated excessively with ornaments, and others held two-headed snakes in their claws. Despite the changes in the way they were depicted, a continuity can be seen in the theme over time, a cultural intention to express similar ideas, even though the objects were made differently. The relationship between birds and snakes was always there, along with the contradiction between flight and the stillness of the central characters. Like the standardisation of figures, the technological variations no

Breastplate in the form of a bird
19.2 X 18.2 CM
SANTA MARTA, MAGDALENA.
SIERRA NEVADA DE SANTA MARTA,
NAHUANGE PERIOD.
200 A.D. – 900 A.D.
O15463

doubt occurred because of social changes that the peoples of the Sierra Nevada underwent around 900 A.D. The golden eagles were perhaps a way of identifying related groups or religious hierarchy differences, or possibly they were used as emblems of power by the peoples of the Sierra. The bird motif has been of great importance over time, and it exists even today among the Koguis and Wiwas, the native peoples of the Sierra Nevada de Santa Marta, in myths about their origin. **JSS**

Pendant in the form of a two-headed bird
5 X 6.2 CM
SIERRA NEVADA
DE SANTA MARTA,
NAHUANGE PERIOD.
200 A.D. - 900 A.D.
O22859

Breastplate in the form of a bird
13.7 X 12.1 CM
SANTA MARTA, MAGDALENA.
SIERRA NEVADA DE SANTA MARTA, TAIRONA PERIOD.
900 A.D. - 1600 A.D.
O09346

12.3 X 9.3 CM
SIERRA NEVADA DE SANTA MARTA, TAIRONA PERIOD.
900 A.D. - 1600 A.D.
O23820

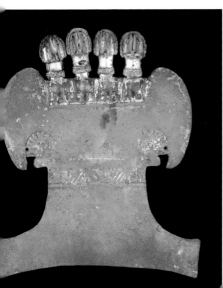

The Stone Cities

A number of major social, economic and political changes occurred in the communities living on the Sierra Nevada de Santa Marta between 600 and 900 A.D. One of the most significant of these was that new population systems were developed. Previously, villages had been scattered all along the coast, but these were gradually replaced by true urban complexes on the mountains, surrounded by intensive corn, cassava and fruit crops, which proved by about 900 A.D. to be an excellent way of adapting to a fragile environment which had to meet the demands of a growing population. A system of paved pathways enabled people to move around, and allowed a wide range of products to be bartered between the coast and the mountains.

The Taironas were concentrated principally in the north western corner of the Sierra, from sea level up to heights of not more than 2,500 metres. This flank of the Sierra boasted areas with fertile soils set amidst rugged terrain, where there were fast-flowing streams. Settlement of this land went hand-in-hand with technological innovations like the large architectural structures with stone foundations.

Terraces supported by retaining walls made of stone were built, in order to make flat areas available on which houses could be erected. These terraces were linked by paths and bridges made of the same material, which were also used as a drainage mechanism for running off rainwater.

Buildings were supported by wooden posts, and they very probably had walls of adobe, wood, palm or bark, and palm or straw roofs, depending on the height above sea level.

Nowadays, the best-known cities are Buritaca 200 (the Lost City), which is an Archaeological Park situated in the upper reaches of the River Buritaca, and Pueblito, in Tayrona National Park, in the River Piedras basin. **JSS**

Lost City
HOUSING PLATFORMS AND STAIRCASES OF THE LOST CITY, A NATIONAL PARK ON THE SIERRA NEVADA DE SANTA MARTA

Anthropo-zoomorphous pendant
6.2 X 6.4 CM
CIÉNAGA, MAGDALENA.
SIERRA NEVADA DE SANTA MARTA,
TAIRONA PERIOD.
900 A.D. - 1600 A.D.
012564

Bat-man modelled in clay
6.4 X 2.7 CM
SIERRA NEVADA DE SANTA MARTA,
TAIRONA PERIOD.
900 A.D. - 1600 A.D.
026177

Shamans who Travel through the Night

During the Tairona Period (900 - 1600 A.D.), images of humans and animals depicted shamans as being capable of demonstrating their power through their ability to transform themselves into different beings and to take on the qualities of those beings: boldness, strength, sharp eyesight, or the ability to fly. Just as it is today with the Koguis, one of the four indigenous groups that live on the Sierra Nevada, transformation had to be a process which went on in the thoughts, under the effect of psychotropic substances, exhausting ritual dances, fasting and other privations typical of the shaman's trade. His spirit could then travel through unknown regions of the cosmos and acquire powers and knowledge that were inaccessible to other members of the community.

The most emblematic of these representations was that of the bat-man. It can be deduced from gold or pottery figures that some shamans gave themselves this appearance by wearing certain ornaments on their faces, while others wore masks which brought out the features of the bat. The fact that these mammals were able to fly at night must have been a not insignificant power.

The shaman's attire consisted of a visor with extensions that simulated the membranes of the animal's ears, a double, cylindrical nose ring which lifted the nasal septum, and sub-labial ornaments to simulate the fleshy tissues of the jaw of certain species. Perforation or chafing of the face was necessary if these accessories were to be used or worn, and this was no doubt the price that had to be paid for achieving the definitive consecration of the bat-man. **JSS**

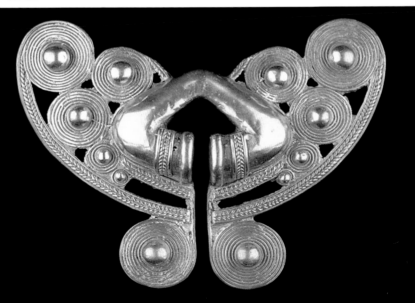

Pendant in the form of a
bat carved in jadeite
16.2 X 2.5 CM
SANTA MARTA, MAGDALENA.
SIERRA NEVADA DE SANTA MARTA,
TAIRONA PERIOD.
900 A.D. - 1600 A.D.
L00584

THE GOLD OF THE SHAMANS AND THE COMMON MAN

A new social order during the Tairona Period imposed strict guidelines for the making and wearing of metal objects. Production was directed towards personal ornaments, and thousands of objects were made that could be worn by everyone. However, certain emblems were reserved exclusively for the elite, such as large, bird-shaped breastplates, or breastplates with figures on them of animal-men loaded down with ornaments. The goldsmiths used alloys of copper and gold. Although they made many hammered ornaments, they preferred to use the lost wax technique, because it was more versatile for decorating figures that had large numbers of ornaments on them. **JSS**

Nose ring
7.1 X 9 CM   SANTA MARTA, MAGDALENA.
SIERRA NEVADA DE SANTA MARTA,
TAIRONA PERIOD.   900 A.D. - 1600 A.D.
O12792

Ceremonial vessel modelled in clay
15.7 X 31.7 CM
SIERRA NEVADA DE SANTA MARTA,
TAIRONA PERIOD.
900 A.D. - 1600 A.D.
C13437

Stick carved
out of stone
104 X 6.6 CM
SANTA MARTA,
MAGDALENA
SIERRA NEVADA
DE SANTA MARTA,
TAIRONA PERIOD
900 A.D. - 1600 A.D.
L03238

Cultural Continuity

The conflict with the Spaniards, which went on throughout virtually the whole of the 16th century, led to a notable decrease in the size of the indigenous population and to their retreating to the highest parts of the Sierra Nevada de Santa Marta, which were inaccessible to the armies and missionaries that attempted to bring them under the colonial regime. For several centuries, while living in relative isolation, these peoples underwent a social and cultural restoration process, which culminated in new ethnic groups being formed on the Sierra Nevada, namely the present-day Koguis, Arhuacos, Wiwas or Arsarios and

Kankuamos. These, who consider themselves to be the older brothers of mankind and heirs to the wisdom and precepts of the ancients, have incorporated cultural elements of different origins into their traditions and customs: pre-Hispanic, Spanish, and more recently, Colombian society.

One feature that all these groups have in common is their strong religious orientation, which has seemingly changed little since the time of the Conquest.

Objects such as stone sticks, monolithic axes, winged plates and masks, which were once part of the ritual paraphernalia used during ceremonies, have been found in the ceremonial buildings of urban centres like the Lost City or Pueblito, where ceremonial activities were performed in pre-Hispanic times. These findings, together with depictions in clay of ceremonies in enclosed areas and the figures of important religious dignitaries such as the bat-man, the jaguar-man and the bird-man, point to a strong theocratic orientation in Tairona society which has survived down to the present day as the focal point around which the organisation of these peoples revolves. JSS

Ceremonial axe carved out of stone
10.9 X 29.4 CM
SANTA MARTA, MAGDALENA
SIERRA NEVADA DE SANTA MARTA,
TAIRONA PERIOD.
900 A.D. - 1600 A.D.
L00042

Winged plate
4.9 X 35.4 CM
SIERRA NEVADA
DE SANTA MARTA,
TAIRONA PERIOD.
900 A.D. - 1600 A.D.
L03465

The Eastern Cordillera – the Muiscas and their Neighbours

At least 15,000 years ago, diverse groups of hunters and gatherers settled on the high plains and on the slopes and in the inter-Andean valleys of the Eastern Cordillera. Their camps, in rocky shelters and on terraces, contain remains of animals such as mastodons and horses, which lived in the region in those days. Over thousands of years, these groups gradually changed their means of subsistence: around 5,000 years ago, they began to grow certain plants, and pottery production commenced about 3,000 years ago.

From 600 A.D. onwards, the region gradually came to be inhabited by various Chibcha-speaking peoples, who migrated from Central America. We do not know very well how these new settlers got on with the natives who lived in the region, but a drastic change in cultural materials can be seen at virtually all housing sites. The Chibchas, who were numerous and who adapted easily to the environmental diversity of the Cordillera, settled on moorland and in regions where the climate was cold or temperate. When the first Europeans reached the high plains in 1537, they found Muiscas, Guanes, Laches and Chitareros living in adjacent territories, alongside other minor groups like Tequias, Teguas, Sutagaos and Duits, about whom they left no precise information. The Muiscas were the most numerous of these. Although all Chibcha peoples were different, with differing ways of life and forms of organisation, all of them used similar objects to express a shared vision of the world and of themselves. The different Chibcha groups kept up economic, ritual and symbolic relations with each other for centuries, and recognised each other as close relatives. Their shamans exchanged knowledge, merchants from the different groups frequently visited regional markets, and the chieftains of the different ethnic groups forged temporary alliances with each other. RLL

Anthropomorphous votive figures.
15.3 X 4.8 CM
17.8 X 4.7 CM
13 X 4.6 CM
EL HOYO, GUTIÉRREZ, CUNDINAMARCA.
EASTERN CORDILLERA, MUISCA - GUANE PERIOD.
1360 A.D.
O33903, O33904, O33905

Guasca, Cundinamarca

Metallurgy Styles

Objects made of gold, copper and alloys of these were manufactured for more than a thousand years in the Eastern Cordillera. The fact that each people followed its own traditions, coupled to diverse manufacturing techniques being employed, meant that an extraordinary variety of ornaments and offering objects was produced. The copper deposits that can be found easily in the region were exploited for this, even though they are not particularly rich. Gold, on the other hand, was obtained by bartering with groups from the Magdalena valley and the Antioquia massif, since there are no gold mines or alluvial gold in the Eastern Cordillera.

Three very different styles can be identified, which correspond to certain geographical areas, and these were used by different people. The first style is that of the cold, high plains, and consists of a group made up of ornaments with fretwork decoration and hanging plates, and of numerous votive figures made by casting using the lost wax method. This type of ornament was worn mostly by political and religious leaders; offering figures are plentiful and varied.

The chieftains who lived in temperate and hot climates - on the western slopes of the Cordillera - wore outfits consisting of large, laminar objects such as breastplates, diadems and nose rings. These form the second style, and a notable feature of these hammered gold and tumbaga objects is the influence of groups from the Magdalena valley and the Central Cordillera.

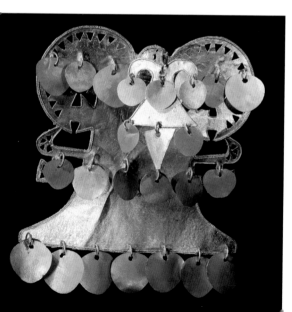

Farmers, artisans, traders and other ordinary people all over the Eastern Cordillera wore small, simple ornaments such as hoop-shaped earrings and half-moon shaped

Breastplate in the form of a bird
11 X 11.9 CM
VARELA, CHIQUINQUIRÁ, BOYACÁ.
EASTERN CORDILLERA,
MUISCA - GUANE PERIOD.
1080 A.D.
033772

**Anthropomorphous
votive figure**
• 9,6 X 2,4 CM
• 8,4 X 2,5 CM
O00293/O04678
EASTERN CORDILLERA,
MUISCA - GUANE PERIOD.
600 A.D. - 1600 A.D.

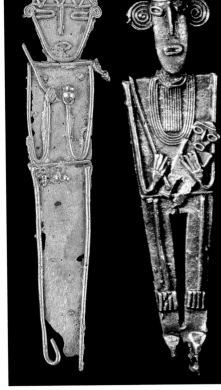

**Earring
pendants**
3.4 AND 3.5 CM
COGUA,
CUNDINAMARCA.
EASTERN CORDILLERA,
MUISCA - GUANE PERIOD.
600 A.D. - 1600 A.D.
O08489 / O08490

Vessel
16.3 X 17.3 CM
EASTERN CORDILLERA,
MUISCA - GUANE PERIOD.
600 A.D. - 1600 A.D.
C00442

141

nose rings. This third style is thus a group of very simple objects made by hammering alluvial gold, which are found in individual graves and frequently show signs of wear and tear due to the intensive use to which they were put. **RLL**

Vessel
30.5 X 24 CM
EASTERN CORDILLERA,
MUISCA - GUANE
PERIOD.
600 A.D. - 1600 A.D.
C10982

Economy and Subsistence

By 1500, the Chibcha groups on the Eastern Cordillera, including the Muiscas, had developed a stable, efficient, agriculture-based economy. The fact that they were able to control different climatic levels, ranging from moorland through cold, high plains down to temperate and hot slopes and valleys, meant they could stock up on a variety of products, and that these would be available throughout the year. Various villages also held periodic markets, where products were bartered under the protection of the chieftains. They thus managed to ensure that groups who specialised in the production of a particular article - clay pots, emeralds, blankets - could exchange them for what they needed. They were accustomed to

Breastplate
9.8 X 13.4 CM
CHIQUINQUIRÁ, BOYACÁ
EASTERN CORDILLERA, MUISCA - GUANE
PERIOD.
1080 A.D.
O33830

Goblet
13.5 X 18.5 CM
EASTERN CORDILLERA, MUISCA -
GUANE PERIOD.
600 A.D. - 1600 A.D.
C12916

people and groups paying tribute to their captains and chieftains, who stored this up in their enclosures so that when some group or other was suffering hardship, the chieftains turned to these surpluses in order to help them.

Salt mining was another very important occupation, and salt was distributed all along the trading routes, even beyond the Cordillera. Other activities engaged in included emerald mining, coca leaf production, and the manufacturing of pottery and metalwork. The textile industry warrants a special mention: cotton growing and spinning, along with blanket weaving, were activities that brought together hundreds of inhabitants of the Eastern Cordillera. The carving and polishing of stone objects, perhaps one of the oldest traditional industries in the region, enabled the Muiscas to ensure that all the necessary instruments were available for their work, such as axes, chisels, awls, hooks, harpoons, and other instruments for cutting and carving wood, scraping and making holes in skins, hunting and fishing.

A few villages, including Guatavita, became metalworking centres, and there the metalsmiths handed down the secrets of the trade from one generation to the next and dealt with orders from distant parts, often having to travel with all their equipment to meet the demands of chieftains and priests. **RLL**

Stone matrix
8.2 X 4.2 CM
EASTERN CORDILLERA,
MUISCA - GUANE
PERIOD.
600 A.D. - 1600 A.D.
L00001

Bench with anthropo-zoomorphous figure
47.2 X 12 CM
EASTERN CORDILLERA, MUISCA - GUANE PERIOD.
600 A.D. - 1600 A.D.
M00138

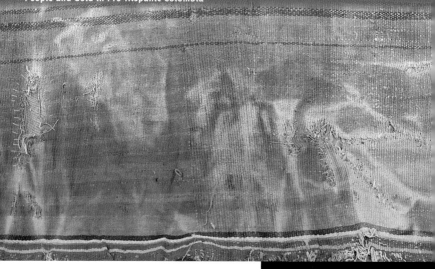

Blanket
131 X 69 CM
EASTERN CORDILLERA,
MUISCA -
GUANE PERIOD.
600 A.D. - 1600 A.D.
T00141

Cap
18 X 23 CM
SANTANDER
EASTERN CORDILLERA,
MUISCA - GUANE PERIOD.
600 A.D. - 1600 A.D.
T00153

Textiles and Weavers

The textile industry was of vital importance to the Chibcha inhabitants of the Eastern Cordillera. Not only was it one of the commonest economic activities of people living at all climatic levels, it also had great symbolic importance. Different vegetable fibres were used, the most important of which were cotton and sisal, as these were grown in the hot and temperate valleys on the mountain slopes. Before blankets, caps, diadems, shoulder bags and nets could be made from these fibres, they first had to be spun, and this was a job that was done by women, using spindles driven by stone whorls. The threads were then woven on wooden looms, some vertical with a frame, others of the belt type. Some fabrics were decorated as they were being woven, using varying combinations of colours in the warp and weft. Others, meanwhile, were decorated with paint, using fine brushes. The decorative motifs which combined circles,

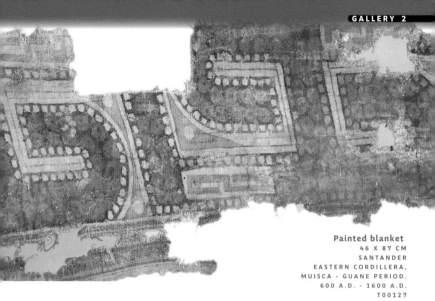

Painted blanket
46 X 87 CM
SANTANDER
EASTERN CORDILLERA,
MUISCA - GUANE PERIOD.
600 A.D. - 1600 A.D.
T00127

triangles, friezes, stripes and rectangles had meanings that today we cannot understand.

There were many types of blankets, from the simplest and smallest to ones that were very large and exquisitely decorated, which could only be worn by chieftains and priests. Blankets were used as tribute, and as gifts for dignitaries and ruling figures. They went on being woven in large quantities even after the Conquest, as they served the same function in the *encomiendas* of the Spanish conquistadors.

One of the most important uses to which blankets were put was in connection with the burying of mummies. The bodies of chieftains, priests and leading figures were wrapped in various layers of blankets, nets and animal skins to make

funerary bundles, which were then deposited inside natural caves in cliffs and rock walls that were hard to get to. Most of the blankets that are preserved in the Gold Museum's collection come from these graves. **RLL**

Shoulder bag
19.5 X 14.4 CM
EASTERN CORDILLERA, MUISCA - GUANE
PERIOD.
600 A.D. - 1600 A.D.
T00137

Offerings and Offering Receptacles

Chibcha life was imbued with profound religious precepts. Religion determined the rules for living together in society and the relationship between the community and nature. One of the most widespread religious practices was the offering. In general terms, the offering is a symbolic exchange, involving material and non-material elements, between a social group and the supernatural forces or beings that the group recognises and worships.

In the case of the Muiscas, material offerings were made of gold, copper, tumbaga, wood, stone and clay, in the form of thousands of figures which their priests (*jeques*) deposited in lakes, caves and fields where crops were grown. The different shapes, sizes and colours of these were perhaps strictly controlled, so that objects were obtained whose precise meanings related to the intention of the particular offering.

Anthropomorphous offering receptacle
49.7 X 10 CM
CHOCONTÁ, CUNDINAMARCA.
EASTERN CORDILLERA,
MUISCA - GUANE PERIOD.
600 A.D. - 1600 A.D.
C12900

Offering receptacle with lid
14.9 X 7.8 CM
FONTIBÓN, CAPITAL DISTRICT.
EASTERN CORDILLERA,
MUISCA - GUANE PERIOD.
600 A.D. - 1600 A.D.
C12599

Anthropomorphous offering receptacle
25.8 X 31.5 CM
PASCA, CUNDINAMARCA.
EASTERN CORDILLERA,
MUISCA - GUANE PERIOD.
600 A.D. - 1600 A.D.
C01183

Offering receptacle
10.8 X 20.5 CM
TOCANCIPÁ, CUNDINAMARCA.
EASTERN CORDILLERA, MUISCA -
GUANE PERIOD.
600 A.D. - 1600 A.D.
C13488

These metal figures are a whole world in miniature, one that is inhabited by men, women and asexual beings. There are chieftains in their enclosures, a caiman with a head in its stomach, dignitaries being carried on litters, lovers entwined in each others' arms, and sacrifices, not to mention a whole host of feline figures, snakes, deer, snails, birds and everyday objects. Most of the votive figures were offered up in groups. Each group very possibly represented a message, one where each object had a meaning. The priests placed the objects inside special pottery containers of differing shapes: human, animal, phallic or hut. **RLL**

OFFERINGS IN OTHER PARTS OF THE WORLD

It was usual for the ancient Jews to offer lambs up to Jehovah. The Greeks did likewise with their gods, while in Rome, terracotta figures were made for use as offerings. Under the temples in the Maya region, and also in Teotihuacan, Monte Albán and other cities in Middle America, plentiful supplies can be found of figurines made of jade, obsidian and clay. Offerings to the guardian gods have been found in Mexico's *Templo Mayor*. And in Peru, offerings were made before the time of the Incas, but the state religion extended the practice and even took it up to the highest peaks in the Andes, where sacrifices and offerings are still being found. **RLL**

Votive sacrifice post
6.8 X 2.3 CM
SANTA HELENA VILLAGE, LA CALERA,
CUNDINAMARCA.
EASTERN CORDILLERA, MUISCA -
GUANE PERIOD.
600 A.D. - 1600 A.D.
O18647

The Mast Sacrifice

The Muiscas made at least three types of ritual sacrifices, aimed at preserving a symbolic equilibrium in the cosmos. The best-known of these was described as the "Mast Sacrifice" by the Spanish chroniclers who reached the region in 1537. Children are said to have been brought up specially for this ritual in a nearby town on the Eastern Plains, and before they reached adolescence they were selected by the priests and taken to the enclosures of the leading chieftains.

Thick, tall wooden posts were erected outside these enclosures, with a basket-shaped structure at the top, rather like the crow's nest on sailing ships; hence the name the Spaniards gave to the sacrifice. On special dates, one of the children who had been chosen was tied to the basket on the 'mast'. The sacrifice was performed from the ground by throwing darts at him and gathering up the blood that ran down the post in bowls. This sacred liquid was then scattered in the direction of the rising sun.

José Domingo Duquesne, a curate who collected Muisca traditions in the 18th century, tells of how it was believed that the children who were sacrificed in this way flew to heaven and could talk to the moon. The Spaniards thought the practice savage and banned it drastically. However, this did not stop thousands of indians being murdered so that gold offerings could be stolen from them, or because they refused to adopt the practices and beliefs of their lords and masters. **RLL**

Votive sacrifice posts
· 9.5 X 1.1 CM
· 12.4 X 1.4 CM
EASTERN CORDILLERA,
MUISCA - GUANE PERIOD.
600 A.D. - 1600 A.D.
004082 / 029286

Mummy
75 X 65 CM
PISBA, BOYACÁ.
EASTERN CORDILLERA,
MUISCA - GUANE PERIOD.
600 A.D. - 1600 A.D.
D00009

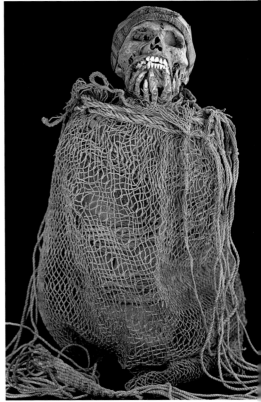

MUMMIES AND MUMMIFICATION

Muiscas, Laches, Guanes and Chitareros all followed the practice of preserving the bodies of important dignitaries. The intention was not only to keep the body intact for the life it would lead in another world, but also to ensure that the person retained a presence in the community. The mummies of chieftains are known to have remained in their former homes, to have been taken out in processions, and to have been consulted as if they were alive. Most bodies that were preserved were placed in deep caves, wrapped in blankets, nets and skins. **RLL**

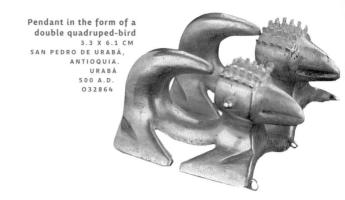

Pendant in the form of a
double quadruped-bird
3.3 X 6.1 CM
SAN PEDRO DE URABÁ,
ANTIOQUIA.
URABÁ
500 A.D.
O32864

Between Two Seas - Urabá and Chocó

The environments along the coasts and river banks and on the plains and in the foothills offered the inhabitants of Urabá and Chocó a variety of different resources for their subsistence, not to mention numerous access routes for travelling around and engaging in trade. Several thousand years earlier, this area had been an entrance point to South America for the first hunters and gatherers.

Later, from the early years of the Christian era, sedentary societies of fishermen, gatherers, farmers and miners modified the landscape and left behind remains of their pottery and metalwork. The present-day Cuna, Embera and Waunana communities are descendants of groups who survived the Spanish Conquest and later underwent profound changes.
MAU

>
Breastplate
16.1 CM
CHOCÓ.
CHOCÓ.
500 A.D. - 1600 A.D.
O32686

>
Mouth of the
River Atrato in
the Gulf of Urabá

Cosmopolitan Urabá

Urabá metalwork shows that their societies were cosmopolitan people who had close links with neighbouring communities and others further away. The human iconography in Quimbaya style and the *poporos* and *poporo* necks in the form of fruits clearly point to links with the Early Quimbaya style in the Cauca basin. At the time of the Conquest, and probably earlier, these regions were joined by a trade route which brought gold and other products to the inhabitants of Urabá. Similarly, spiral breastplates, zoomorphous pendants with raised tail and other ornaments indicate connections with the Caribbean Plains, the Sierra Nevada de Santa Marta, Panama and Costa Rica, where similar artefacts are known, albeit with clear local traits. It is believed from this evidence that Central American metallurgists learned their trade from their neighbours in Urabá, and that these common elements in their material culture were used to create and manifest identities and links between the people.

But Urabá metalwork is also notable for features that are entirely its own, such as a recurring use of the spiral, a natural form which inspired the metalsmiths to create a vast range of original designs. **MAU**

Nose ring with spirals
5.4 X 4 CM
URABÁ
200 A.D. - 1600 A.D.
O29665

152

Pendant in the form of a bird-man
4.7 X 3.9 CM
SAN PEDRO DE URABÁ,
ANTIOQUIA. URABÁ
200 A.D. - 1600 A.D.
O32333

<
Breastplate
9.2 X 17.2 CM
SAN PEDRO DE URABÁ,
ANTIOQUIA. URABÁ
200 A.D. - 1600 A.D.
O31834

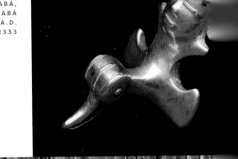

A GOLD BAMBOO POPORO

Urabá metalwork includes a lime container shaped like a *guadua* (bamboo, *Bambusa guadua*) shoot, perhaps copied from *poporos* that were actually made from this species of bamboo. It is a unique object in Colombian metalwork, despite the fact that the *guadua* variety of bamboo was an essential material for pre-Hispanic societies, especially in their architecture. But why make a bamboo *poporo* out of gold? Different materials have their own particular meanings and associations in all cultures; gold and bamboo were probably related in Urabá to different ideas and different social groups. MAU

Lime container shaped like bamboo
25 X 5.5 CM
SAN PEDRO DE URABÁ,
ANTIOQUIA. URABÁ
200 A.D. - 1600 A.D.
O33476

Darién pendant
11.4 X 9.5 CM
RIVER PURRICHÁ,
UPPER BAUDÓ, CHOCÓ.
CHOCÓ
500 A.D. - 1600 A.D.
O06815

Darién Pendants from Chocó

The Museum's collection includes a small group of metalwork objects from the Pacific coast of Chocó, made up of anthropomorphous ornaments referred to as "Darién pendants". They are a sort of schematised depiction that was common over much of the territory now known as Colombia for a long time. Most are made of metal, but there are also some that are made of clay and shell. Apart from their shared features, they depict distinctive elements from different regions and periods, as if it were an icon that was reinterpreted and given new meaning in accordance with particular cultural codes. The Darién pendants from Chocó are notable for their large size and the fact that they were made carefully from gold with a high assay value, and the figures depicted have angled shoulders and are wearing a mask with spirals.

These figures have been interpreted in many different ways: they could be a crocodile god, bat-men, or shamans wearing ritual attire. Most probably, however, different peoples gave them different meanings and put them to different uses, since the meanings of the artefacts are not intrinsic to them, but rather are being negotiated all the time by those who appropriate them socially. **MAU**

THE ANCIENT GOLD TRADE IN CHOCÓ

Chocó is one of the richest regions of Colombia in terms of alluvial gold, and the extraction and bartering of this dates back to ancient times. It has been discovered from nose rings found on archaeological digs in Cupica that gold could have been extracted as long ago as 500 A.D. Some researchers have suggested that around 700 A.D., when gold replaced shell as the preferred material for making prestigious objects in what is now Panamanian territory, Chocó communities could have begun intensive trading activities with people living on Panama bay, to meet the great demand for the precious metal. MAU

Darién pendant with spiral mask
17 X 14.2 CM
CHOCÓ
500 A.D. - 1600 A.D.
O06030

From Columbus...

In 1492, two continents that had been cut off from each other for a long time came into contact once more. The conquest wars and disease decimated the indigenous population, who were then subjected to colonial tribute in agricultural work, transport and mining activities. Many objects were melted down, in view of the prevailing mercantile view of gold and the new religion. Since the 19th century, the remains of the past have encouraged people to study the ancient history of this territory.

... to the Present Day

Colombia has a history which goes back 15,000 years. Pre-Hispanic societies have left us a valuable legacy in the form of various organisational methods, adaptations and ways of thinking. There are currently 84 indigenous groups in the country, who speak 64 native languages. Most have retained their religion, and some of them use gold in their rituals that has been handed down from their forefathers.

Pre-Hispanic metalwork bears testimony to great diversity, yet it offers no more than a sample of the variety of societies that lived and created in this land for thousands of years. After the encounter with the Old World, the influence of European and African peoples was added to the indigenous legacy. EL

Sikuani shaman, Orinoco Plains
PHOTO: FERNANDO URBINA

Tatuyo Indian from the Pirá-Paraná River
PHOTO: Gerardo Reichel Dolmatoff

Cosmology and Symbolism in Metalworking Societies

Figure sitting on a bench
11.8 X 11.5 CM
PACIFIC COAST, INGUAPÍ PERIOD.
700 B.C. - 350 A.D.
C13444

Anthropomorphous vessel.
24.5 X 14.4 CM
MID-CAUCA, LATE PERIOD.
700 A.D. - 1600 A.D.
C00545

*M*ETALWORKING SOCIETIES developed cosmologies, or particular ways of understanding the world, and it was through these that they gave order to their surroundings and endowed nature, their social organisation and their culture with rich symbolic meanings. As is customary in indigenous thought, those cosmologies were imbued with a deep religious sense, and this gave the universe, their territory, society and their material creations a sacred nature. These views also established a close link between men and their ancestors, which was essential if their traditions were to continue and be handed down.

Chieftains, priests, shamans and other specialists had the task of guarding, transmitting and renewing cosmogonic representations. They were persons with special abilities and sensibilities, who were subjected from childhood to long, arduous learning processes about mythology, sacred plants, astronomy and other areas of knowledge, under the guidance of ancient masters and wise men. With their words, gestures and objects as tools, these specialists did a demanding symbolic job, one which set out to transform the world in order to guarantee the wellbeing of their society, and that nature would reproduce. **MAU**

Vessel with anthropo-zoomorphous
figures in the base
19.5 X 26.3 CM
SIERRA NEVADA DE SANTA MARTA,
NAHUANGE PERIOD.
200 A.D. - 900 A.D.
C05615

GALLERY 3

Images of the Cosmos

We can certainly not talk of all metalworking societies having had a single view of the world, although many of them clearly shared similar ideas, due to contacts and dialogues throughout their history, and the fact that they shared common cultural roots. Evidence points to many having held the view that the cosmos was made up of various superimposed, connected and interdependent levels or worlds, each with its own individual properties and beings; certain colours, smells, animals, plants and spirits would be associated with each one. The universe consisted of one material, visible dimension, and another that was spiritual, powerful, and hidden to most people.

Colombian pre-Hispanic metalwork includes objects which appear to depict cosmogonic images. Embossed Nahuange Period breastplates from the Sierra Nevada de Santa Marta portray male characters in a spread-eagled posture, decked out with ornaments and large, fan-shaped headdresses, who are borne aloft on poles by humanoid figures; they are accompanied by bats, birds, reptiles and other animals. Some scholars believe this character depicted the sun deity in his annual journey across the horizon between the two solstices. The positions the animals and other beings are in seem to correspond to a cosmogonic order, with the bats in the underworld and the birds higher up. **MAU**

Breastplate with anthropomorphous figure
11.8 X 11.5 CM
MINCA, SANTA
MARTA, MAGDALENA.
SIERRA NEVADA
DE SANTA MARTA,
NAHUANGE PERIOD.
200 A.D. - 900 A.D.
013977

Breastplate with anthropomorphous figure
12.4 X 13.9 CM
MINCA, SANTA MARTA, MAGDALENA.
SIERRA NEVADA DE SANTA MARTA, NAHUANGE PERIOD.
200 A.D. - 900 A.D.
O15451

This figure, which is on the breastplate in the photo,
probably depicted the Sun on its annual trajectory across
the horizon

Crab-shaped *alcarraza*
22.4 X 12.1 CM
CALIMA REGION,
MALAGANA PERIOD.
200 B.C. - 200 A.D.
C13471

Classifications of Nature

Cosmologies imposed order on natural and social surroundings. The animals, plants, stars and other beings in the world were classified in an orderly manner, using systems based around criteria selected by the particular society. Those criteria could include such varied aspects as habitat, food, cultural customs and habits, and morphology traits. One important feature of certain ancient classification systems appears from the material culture images of some societies to have been whether the different entities were in the sky, on the surface of the earth, in water or in caves, or whether they moved between two different such areas.

Cosmologies also dictated rules governing relations with nature. It is perhaps a general characteristic of indigenous societies that indigenous man views himself as being part of his surroundings; the society and its natural environment make up a single unit, where interactions between beings are viewed as following the model for relations between people. Hunting is often considered to be an act where the hunter seduces his prey, or a reciprocal human relationship that demands retribution from the hunter, which could be in the form of a chant, a dance or an offering. MAU

Staff finial in the form of a heron
14.2 X 15.5 CM
CARIBBEAN PLAINS, ZENÚ TRADITION.
490 A.D.
O29806

Pendant in the form of a two-headed deer.
7.8 X 9.9 CM
MAJAGUAL, SUCRE
CARIBBEAN PLAINS, ZENÚ TRADITION.
200 B.C. - 1600 A.D.
O07504

Pendant in the form of a fish
19.2 X 6.5 CM
CAÑO VILORIA, SAN MARCOS,
SUCRE.
CARIBBEAN PLAINS,
ZENÚ TRADITION.
200 B.C. - 1600 A.D.
O33624

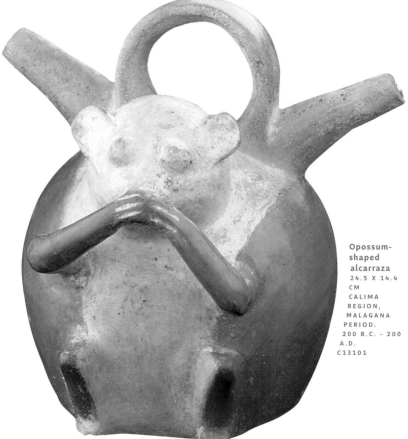

Opossum-shaped alcarraza
24.5 X 14.4 CM
CALIMA REGION, MALAGANA PERIOD.
200 B.C. - 200 A.D.
C13101

Votive figure in the form of an enclosure with two-headed man
9.1 X 5.7 CM
CARMEN DE CARUPA, CUNDINAMARCA.
EASTERN CORDILLERA, MUISCA - GUANE PERIOD.
600 A.D. - 1600 A.D.
O32866

The Symbolism of the Chieftains

Socio-political organisation also had its place in cosmogonic portrayals. Power groups and hierarchical relations were the subject matter of rich symbolic productions, which manifested themselves in taboos, rituals, myths and objects, and in controls over goods and people. Chieftains and other dignitaries were frequently considered to be descendants of divinities like the Sun, and to be related to powerful beings such as the jaguar. In some societies, it was forbidden to look them in the face, while in many, because of their heavenly nature, the "earth taboo" was common: their feet were not allowed to touch the ground, and they had to be carried everywhere on their benches or borne aloft on poles.

It was customary for these ruling figures to have various wives and a retinue of servants, who they lived with in large or several houses surrounded by palisades. They alone had access to certain ornaments, generally those made of gold and other metals, and to certain foods, such as venison. When they died, they were mummified or prepared for burial with very special care, and they were deposited in large tombs under burial mounds or in their enclosures, which from then on became shrines or memorial sites. **MAU**.

Votive figure in the form of a deer
5.4 X 1.7 CM
CARMEN DE CARUPA, CUNDINAMARCA.
EASTERN CORDILLERA, MUISCA -
GUANE PERIOD.
600 A.D. - 1600 A.D.
O33078

Circular earring pendants with anthropomorphous figures
· 9 CM
· 9.2 CM
VARELA, CHIQUINQUIRÁ, BOYACÁ.
EASTERN CORDILLERA,
MUISCA - GUANE PERIOD.
1080 A.D.
O33767 / O33768

The Prestige of the Exotic

Exotic goods or goods that were particularly rare because they were scarce in nature or came from a long way away were viewed as prestige objects of elite members in virtually all pre-Hispanic societies, because it was through them that they could express their control over resources and people, and their links with mythical, distant places. It was common in metalworking societies for chieftains to possess and show off exotic goods: feathers of toucans, parrots and other colourful birds brought from the jungles and the Eastern Plains, sea snails imported from the coast, emeralds mined in the Eastern Cordillera, and gold, resins, fine woods and hallucinogenic substances from various places. **MAU**

Carved emerald
4 X 2.5 CM
E00009

Anthropomorphous votive figure with bird headdress
10.3 X 5.3 CM
EASTERN CORDILLERA,
MUISCA -
GUANE PERIOD.
600 A.D. - 1600 A.D.
001861

Bowl with deer-man figure
9.1 X 17.8 CM
NARIÑO HIGH PLAINS,
LATE PERIOD
600 A.D. - 1600 A.D.
C05522

The Body-Apparel and Transformation

There is no radical difference between humans and non-humans in many Amerindian visions of the cosmos. Persons, animals, plants, rocks and objects are people, albeit different types of people, and all of them share a common soul or spirit. Tapir-people, fish-people and the rest all live in communities, harvest, have their homes, and dance like men. Each people type has a particular way of viewing the world, its own perspective, which is determined by its body, a body-apparel that can be removed and changed at will. Putting on feathers or ornaments or painting the body means changing the body-apparel and transforming the view of the world.

The figures that Colombian archaeologists frequently find of beings with human and animal traits, and of persons wearing animal attire, suggest that similar ideas existed in the past. It appears from these objects that different societies gave priority to certain transformations: on the Sierra Nevada de Santa Marta, for example, the bat-man was all-important, while with the Muiscas, it was bird-men, and in the south west, the jaguar-man was common during the first thousand years after Christ. Mixtures appear in other regions, of humans combined with deer, crabs, snakes or snails. **MAU**

168

Votive figure in the
form of a snake with an
anthropomorphic head
4.6 X 3.1 CM
EASTERN CORDILLERA,
MUISCA - GUANE PERIOD.
600 A.D. - 1600 A.D.
002130

Ornament for the arm in
the form of a crab-man
18 X 15.3 CM
PALMIRA, VALLE DEL
CAUCA
CALIMA REGION,
MALAGANA PERIOD.
200 B.C. - 200 A.D.
033393

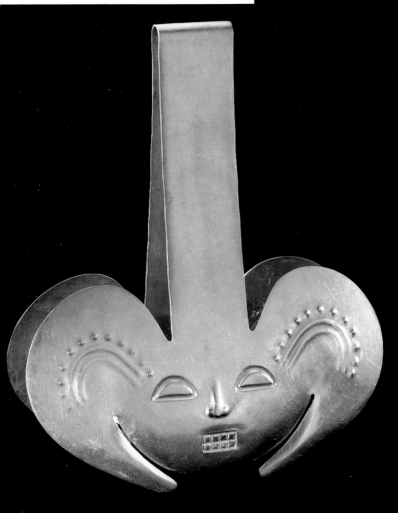

Ornaments to Change Identity

Much Colombian pre-Historic metalwork is in the form of body ornaments, notably nose rings, earrings, pendants and breastplates. These objects served various functions: they reinforced aesthetic, status-building, gender and other social characteristics of the individual person, or were used for transforming his identity.

As it was with many indigenous groups throughout the world, the perception held by some metalworking peoples of the person himself and of reality was transformed many times during the person's life. Ornaments and apparel helped construct each new identity; when the person was dressed up as an animal, plant, ancestor or mythical spirit, he took on the names, skills and principal characteristics of those species or beings. With tubular nose rings and a metal visor to convert him into a vampire-man, he sucked blood, acquired nocturnal habits and saw the word upside down; as a bird-man, decked out with feathers and ornaments with birds on them, he took to flight and acquired sharp eyesight so he could hunt.

Although it depended on what was depicted on them, metal ornaments were used primarily for transforming people into animals. Some, with corn or flower shapes on them, could turn people into plants, conjuring up ideas of bodies made from corn, cassava or coca that indigenous groups today have. Unusually-shaped ornaments could transform people into an ancestor or other divinities. **MAU**

Corn-shaped ear spools
6.7 CM, 6.7 CM
SAN JOSÉ DE ISNOS,
HUILA.
SAN AGUSTÍN, REGIONAL
CLASSICAL PERIOD.
1 A.D. - 900 A.D.
032871, 032872

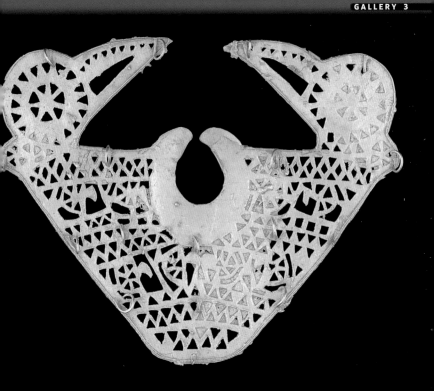

Fretwork nose ring
with bird heads
14.6 X 18.9 CM
BOYACÁ
EASTERN CORDILLERA,
MUISCA - GUANE PERIOD.
600 A.D. - 1600 A.D.
O33882

Staff finial in the form
of a crab's claw
11.3 X 8.2 CM
SANTIAGO BAJO, PLANETA
RICA, CÓRDOBA.
CARIBBEAN PLAINS,
ZENÚ TRADITION.
200 B.C. - 1600 A.D.
O33147

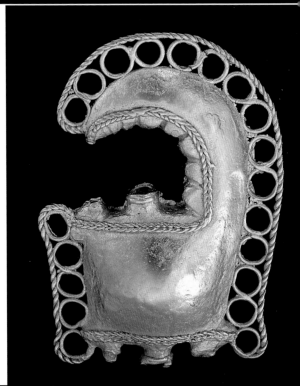

**Mask in the shape
of a feline figure**
8.7 X 12.8 CM
EL PEDREGAL,
INZÁ, CAUCA.
TIERRADENTRO,
MIDDLE PERIOD.
150 A.D. - 900
A.D.
007354

Feline Men

The jaguar has been a symbol associated with religion and power in America since time immemorial. Because of its sagacity, aggressiveness and strength, not to mention its golden colour, it has been associated with other natural, supernatural and social bodies and phenomena, such as the Sun, gold, thunder, caverns, fire, priests, and governing figures. Artefacts produced by metalworking societies, of which there are countless examples with jaguars depicted on them, are clear evidence of the symbolic importance those societies placed on this animal.

In pre-Hispanic times and during the Conquest, high-ranking persons had names which alluded to feline figures, wore clothing made from the skins of such animals and masks and ornaments depicting their features, painted their bodies to imitate the animals' spots, and wore loincloths with long tails. Some also let

**Pendant in the form
of a jaguar**
7.5 X 12.2 CM
EL BANCO, MAGDALENA.
CARIBBEAN PLAINS,
ZENÚ TRADITION.
350 A.D.
017191

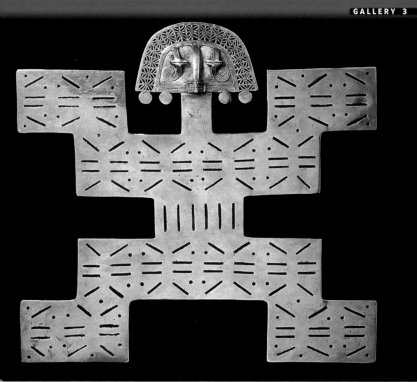

their nails grow long to look like claws, and at the same time show that mundane activities were beneath them. The Spanish chroniclers tell of how chieftains and priests were transformed into "big cats" and communicated with jaguar spirits during their ceremonies. This elaborate symbolism resulted in feline-men being treated with deep respect and obedience. **MAU**

Breastplate in the form of a jaguar-man
23.4 X 25.7 CM
EL DRAGÓN,
CALARCÁ,
QUINDÍO.
MID-MAGDALENA
VALLEY,
MIDDLE PERIOD.
1 B.C. - 700 A.D.
O06029

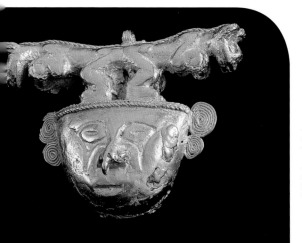

Anthropomorphous pendant with feline figures
5.4 X 7.3 CM
CARIBBEAN PLAINS,
ZENÚ TRADITION.
200 B.C. - 1600 A.D.
O33141

Plants of Knowledge

Pre-Hispanic societies handled a vast range of plants, some of which had important religious uses. Shamans and other specialists in sacred matters used sacred plants like tobacco, coca, *yagé*, *yopo* and many more to help them immerse themselves in the spiritual dimension of reality, visit other levels of the cosmos, and communicate with all beings there. Consuming these plants, coupled to fasting, sound and light effects and repeated body movements, induced a state of trance which made the invisible visible and taught them the secrets of the universe. Because they have these special functions, these plants are imagined in the indigenous world to be a component of the soul and its spiritual nourishment, as well as being the primary source of wisdom and power.

Shamans and priests were experts in processing and using sacred plants, in the cultural purposes of these, and in recognising the different spirits they encountered in their trances. Countless objects are to be found in the material culture of metalworking societies that were used as aids in the consumption of these plants. Often profusely decorated, they were an essential part of the shaman's paraphernalia: snuff trays, *poporos*, lime sticks, pipes, inhalers and spoons, all made from materials as diverse as metal, clay, wood, bone and shell.

MAU

**Pipe with
zoomorphous figure**
11.8 X 4.6 CM
CALIMA REGION,
YOTOCO PERIOD.
200 B.C. - 1300 A.D.
C03972

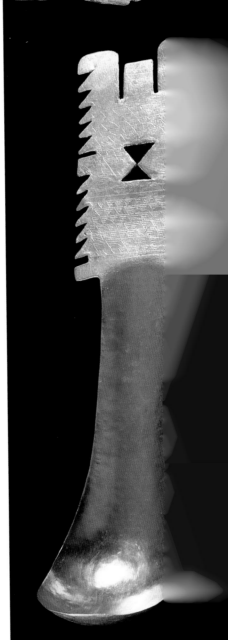

Hallucinogen tray with feline figures, made of wood
2.2 X 13.2 CM
EASTERN CORDILLERA, MUISCA - GUANE PERIOD.
600 A.D. - 1600 A.D.
M00129

Spoon with geometric adornment
22.5 X 4.4 CM
RESTREPO, VALLE DEL CAUCA.
CALIMA REGION, YOTOCO PERIOD.
200 B.C. - 1300 A.D.
O06284

Lime container made of stone in the form of a snail with the figure of a monkey
6.5 X 4.1 CM
NARIÑO HIGH PLAINS, LATE PERIOD.
600 A.D. - 1600 A.D.
L00902

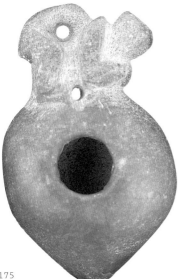

Lime stick with rattle head
23.8 X 3.7 CM
MADROÑAL, RESTREPO,
VALLE DEL CAUCA
CALIMA REGION, YOTOCO PERIOD
200 B.C. - 1300 A.D.
O05701

Coca and the Word

Two varieties of coca have been grown in Colombia since very ancient times. *Coca novogranatense*, or Colombian coca, is grown today by indigenous groups in the Andean Region and on the Sierra Nevada de Santa Marta, and when the leaves have been roasted, they are mixed with lime extracted from sea shells, which are burned and crushed, before being chewed. The lime is kept in a special container made from a marrow or gourd which is called a *poporo*, and it is removed from this with a wooden stick that has first been moistened with saliva. In the Amazon Region, it is *Coca ipadu* that is chewed: the crushed, roasted leaves are mixed with ash from the leaves of the trumpetwood tree (*Cecropia sp.*), and kept in bags or tree-gourds. This ash is rich in calcium and, like lime, helps improve the stimulating effect of the plant. The fact that archaeological

Lime container in the form of a feline figure
6.5 X 13.3 CM
MADROÑAL, RESTREPO, VALLE DEL CAUCA.
CALIMA REGION, YOTOCO PERIOD.
200 B.C. - 1300 A.D.
O00029

many other regions includes numerous *poporos* and sticks is evidence in itself of the widespread chewing of the *novogranatense* variety in pre-Hispanic times.

Coca has a special psychotropic effect, one which stimulates the memory and speech while diminishing tiredness and hunger. It was because of these effects that American peoples used it frequently during long recitals of their myths and traditions, and associated it with shamans and other specialists in sacred oratory. It is revealing that present-day indigenous communities in the Amazon refer to coca as "words". **MAU**

Lime container in the form of a crocodile-man
16.5 X 5.2 CM
LA PRADERA, VALLE DEL CAUCA.
CALIMA REGION, MALAGANA PERIOD.
200 B.C. - 200 A.D.
O33338, O33339

Coca plant
Erithroxylum sp.

Yopo, a Powerful Hallucinogen

Yopo, a powerful hallucinogen that is extracted from the *Anadenanthera* tree, was widely used in pre-Hispanic times by Chibcha groups in the Eastern Cordillera, and today it is an essential component of religious life for the Uwas, one of the groups descended from them. *Yopo* reached this region from the Eastern Plains, through bartering. The seeds were ground, and the resulting powder was inhaled with the help of a small spoon, bird bone or metal pipe from small wooden or metal trays. The Museum's collection includes an outstanding set of Muisca-style trays decorated with feline figures, birds and snakes, animals which

anyone taking the snuff probably got transformed into. A toucan beak made of tumbaga was perhaps used for keeping the powder in; we know that the Uwas used the beaks of this bird until quite recently for this purpose.

Yopo and other sacred plants were often used in prophesying and curing rituals. The chronicler Simón bears this out, since when speaking of Muisca priests, he says that *"when they do their witchcraft, they sniff these powders and get them right up their nose, and as they sting, they make the mucus run right down to their mouth; then they look in the mirror, and if it runs straight it is a good sign for what they attempt to prophesy, but if it twists, then it is the opposite"*. **MAU**

Hallucinogen container in the form of a bird's beak
15.3 X 3.6 CM
SAN MIGUEL, FUSAGASUGÁ, CUNDINAMARCA.
EASTERN CORDILLERA,
MUISCA - GUANE PERIOD.
600 A.D. - 1600 A.D.
O06092

THE THINKER'S TRAY

The Museum's collection includes a tray for inhaling *yopo* that is decorated with the figure of a man sitting with his legs bent and his hands around his knees. This same posture appears on votive figures as well, and could have referred to the Muiscas' priests or *jeques*, who exercised control over knowledge and the taking of this snuff. In the case of present-day indigenous groups, this posture, which is known as the "basket position", is associated with thinking, and with receiving and keeping in the basket-body the teachings of the shamans. **MAU**

Hallucinogen tray with anthropomorphous figure
3 X 4.3 CM
EL HOYO, GUTIÉRREZ, CUNDINAMARCA.
EASTERN CORDILLERA, MUISCA - GUANE PERIOD.
1360 A.D.
O33900

Hallucinogen tray decorated with feline figure, and corresponding inhaler.
2.2 X 10 CM
VARELA, CHIQUINQUIRÁ, BOYACÁ.
EASTERN CORDILLERA, MUISCA - GUANE PERIOD.
1080 A.D.
O33780

Offerings and Sacrifices to the Immortals

Indigenous cosmogonies ascribe a supernatural origin to much of what goes on in the universe: a natural catastrophe is caused by a furious spirit, sickness is sent by an enemy shaman, and when animals reproduce, it is because their invisible owners have intervened. In order to control these dangerous and ambivalent forces and direct them so they themselves could benefit, people had to act according to the laws of their ancestors and make offerings and sacrifices: offering up gifts of gold, emeralds, coca, birds and human beings as spiritual nourishment to the immortals.

The spirits revealed to shamans what offerings were appropriate during prophesying rituals, together with the place and time where each one should be made. Offerings were often deposited in sacred places where communication was possible with other worlds, such as caves and lakes. Some groups made human sacrifices; the victim was tied high up on sturdy posts at the entrance to their enclosures and pierced with arrows, his blood feeding the living body-home of

the chieftain. Sacrifice, war and hunting were viewed as predatory acts that were both destructive and creative, because for a new life to be created, another one had to be sacrificed. **MAU**

Staff finial made of bone in the form of a
jaguar-man with human and bird figures
6.8 X 5.3 CM
SIERRA NEVADA DE SANTA MARTA, TAIRONA PERIOD.
900 A.D. - 1600 A.D.
H00123

Staff finial in the form of a feline
figure confronting a crocodile
3.9 X 6.1 CM
GUARANDA, MAJAGUAL, SUCRE.
CARIBBEAN PLAINS, LATE ZENÚ PERIOD.
1000 A.D. - 1600 A.D.
O32101

Staff finial made of shell in
the form of a bird of prey
5.5 X 4 CM
K00882

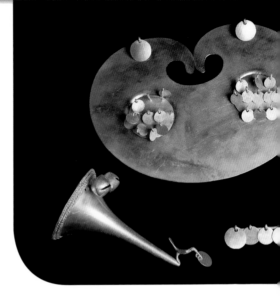

Miniature mask
1.3 X 1.2 CM
SEGUNVITA, TUMACO,
NARIÑO.
PACIFIC COAST,
INGUAPÍ PERIOD.
700 B.C. - 350 A.D.
O33682

The Destiny of Souls

Death was often considered by Amerindian societies to be a transformation into another being or a rebirth, and an event that was necessary in order to prolong life. Some people's souls were reincarnated after death in a bear, a bat, or some other being, and in this new form they went elsewhere, to live on the moors or in caves. For some, the deceased were reborn in tombs, caves or burial mounds and remained near their relatives, intervening in their lives; the chronicles tell of how their descendants talked to them through canes and offered them food and drink. In other societies, the ashes of the dead or their exhumed bones were buried in funerary urns where the deceased was reborn, an idea that was implicit in Mid-Cauca funerary urns, which were shaped like pregnant women about to give birth.

Some groups mummified their chieftains, including the Muiscas and other groups in the Eastern Cordillera, and they displayed their mummies at ceremonies and in wars, so they could protect the community and instil valour in their warriors. Others symbolically perpetuated their ruling figures by covering them with masks and gold ornaments. The bodies of these dignitaries were buried or kept under mounds or in shrines, caves and other special places where their successors and heirs could establish links with powerful and memorable ancestors. **MAU**

Funerary attire: breastplate, bracelets, nose ring and loincloth.
PLANETA RICA, CÓRDOBA.
CARIBBEAN PLAINS, ZENÚ TRADITION.
200 B.C. - 1600 A.D.
O33161-5

Funerary urn with male figure on a small bench.
76.5 X 59 CM
CUNDINAMARCA.
MID-MAGDALENA VALLEY, LATE PERIOD.
700 A.D. - 1600 A.D.
C13503

Masks of Immortality

Because it does not change with the passing of time, and also because of its particular colour, shine and malleability, many ancient societies around the world used gold to symbolically immortalise the bodies of their most illustrious dead. Pharaohs, kings, priests, military leaders and other dignitaries who warranted passing to the worlds beyond both in body and in soul by virtue of their exploits in their earthly or supernatural lives were covered with sarcophagi, masks and objects made of gold, or which appeared to have been made of this metal.

Some societies in south western Colombia, particularly in the Calima and Malagana region in the early years of the Christian era, used gold masks to immortalise the faces of their leading figures. While Calima masks are generally smaller and sometimes depict paint on the face or monkey figures, those from Malagana sport headdresses and are large and more schematic, to the point where some are totally lacking in features. The metalsmiths made them by hammering large sheets of gold, and then cutting and embossing them. **M A U**

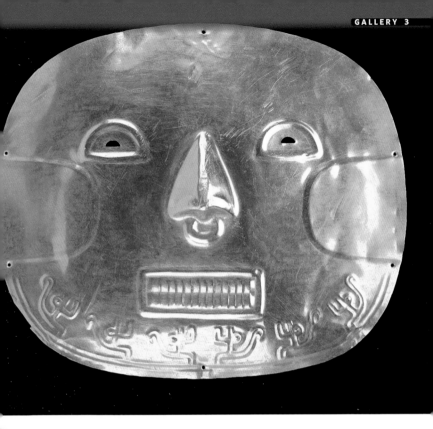

**Funerary mask with
monkey figures**
25.2 X 31 CM
SAN SALVADOR, RESTREPO,
VALLE DEL CAUCA.
CALIMA REGION, YOTOCO PERIOD.
200 B.C. - 1300 A.D.
O05369

Funerary mask with headdress
32 X 53 CM
PALMIRA, VALLE DEL CAUCA.
CALIMA REGION,
MALAGANA PERIOD.
200 B.C. - 200 A.D.
O33402

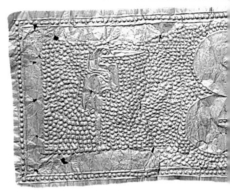

Belt with snake and anthropomorphous head
13.2 X 53.2 CM
RÍO DON DIEGO,
MAGDALENA,
SANTA MARTA.
SIERRA NEVADA
DE SANTA MARTA,
TAIRONA PERIOD.
900 A.D. - 1600 A.D.
O30198

Myths and Rituals for Renewing the World

Stories of the origin of the universe and of the culture in the remote past were told in myths. These explained the genesis of the world, the stars, people and animals, and how the different social groups had obtained their land, tools, musical instruments and marriage rules. Rituals portrayed this mythology through music and dance, thus recreating and renewing the world.

Metalworking societies expressed elements of their mythology and ritual life in their material culture. In their artefacts we see figures wearing complex finery, hybrid beings and scenes with dancers who appear to evoke characters and events from supernatural worlds. Moreover, oral tradition - which the Spaniards noted down at the time of the Conquest - suggests that mythical images were present in certain artefacts, such as Muisca peoples' votive figures of snakes, which were sometimes twin- or double-headed. According to the chronicles, the myth relating to the origin of these groups told of a woman, Bachué, and a child who emerged at the beginning of time from Iguaque lake and then, after populating the world with their offspring, returned to this same lake, converted into snakes. **MAU**

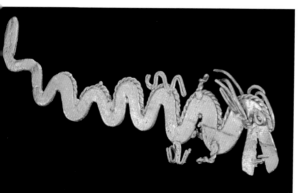

Votive figure in the form of a snake
7.2 X 1.8 CM
RÍO FRIO, CAJICÁ,
CUNDINAMARCA.
EASTERN
CORDILLERA, MUISCA
- GUANE PERIOD.
600 A.D. - 1600 A.D.
O06750

186

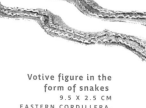

Votive figure in the
form of snakes
9.5 X 2.5 CM
EASTERN CORDILLERA,
MUISCA - GUANE PERIOD.
600 A.D. - 1600 A.D.
O01122

Goblet decorated
with snakes
15 X 20.5 CM
BELÉN, BOYACÁ.
EASTERN CORDILLERA,
MUISCA - GUANE PERIOD.
600 A.D. - 1600 A.D.
C12846

The Dances of the Spirits

When indigenous peoples danced and sang at their periodic rituals, they were summoning the spirits to their party, in order to restate the cosmic order. The dancers, with their masks and finery, were transformed into the creators and into the ancestors, and during the dance, they revived the exploits of the earliest times to the beat of the primeval music. In Amerindian societies today, music and dance not only recreate myths and regenerate the world, they cause animals to reproduce, protect people, and foster happiness and health.

Some Colombian archaeological artefacts were part of ritual paraphernalia. Notable amongst these are the musical instruments, which include flutes, trumpets, whistles and maracas, made from diverse materials. Music recreated the sounds of the origin and helped form a suitable emotional and sensory environment for identifying and communicating with the gods, the universe and the community. **MAU**

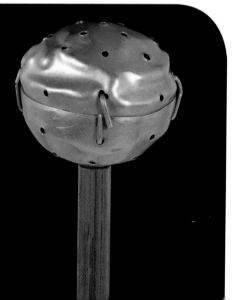

Maraca
4.8 X 5.5 CM
RESTREPO, VALLE DEL CAUCA.
CALIMA REGION, YOTOCO PERIOD.
200 B.C. - 1300 A.D.
007575

188

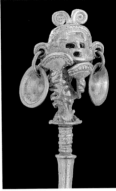

<
Bell made from stone
10.5 X 6.5 CM
SIERRA NEVADA DE SANTA
MARTA, TAIRONA PERIOD.
900 A.D. - 1600 A.D.
L01612

Lime stick with
anthropomorphous head
27.5 X 2.5 CM
CALIMA REGION,
YOTOCO PERIOD.
200 B.C. - 1300 A.D.
O06165

A MASKED BALL

The Museum's collection includes a set of vessels on which Tairona Period potters on the Sierra Nevada de Santa Marta depicted some of their cultures' most important rituals. One of the most elaborate objects, even though coarsely made, portrays a dance, perhaps held inside a shrine, where the five oldest participants are each wearing a large mask with prominent nose and jaws. These masks, together with those on other related vessels, are like various wooden ones preserved in collections, some of which are very ancient, having been made around 1500 A.D., according to radiocarbon dating of the wood. In the centre of the scene can be seen a sort of container and two smaller figures, apparently children. **MAU**

Vessel with
masked figures
12.4 X 22.7 CM
SIERRA NEVADA
DE SANTA
MARTA,
TAIRONA
PERIOD.
900 A.D.
- 1600 A.D.
C13451

Cosmogonic Technologies and Craftsmen

Amerindian peoples gave materials, tools and techniques symbolic meanings, and attributed metalsmiths, potters and others who transformed raw materials with having special powers. Materials were often perceived and thought of as being the sacred beginnings of life, as embryos or beings in formation, which artisans and craftsman helped transform or grow through their work and instruments and the use of fire, as if they were demigods. Metal, clay and stone were symbolised on the basis of their colour, smell, shape and sound. These sensory characteristics were deemed to be a manifestation of their most deeply-concealed spiritual qualities and powers. Furnaces, crucibles and other workshop structures were seen as being places where complex and dangerous transformations occurred, and this is why offerings were made and rituals performed near them, in order to favour the different processes. **MAU**

Crucible
3.6 X 7 CM
PACIFIC COAST, INGUAPí PERIOD.
700 B.C. - 350 A.D.
C12902

**Pendant with pyrite
incrustation**
5.4 X 6 CM
CALIMA REGION,
YOTOCO PERIOD.
200 B.C. - 1300 A.D.
O04126

Necklace made of
stone beads
176 CM
L03453

Colour in the Past

In recent years, archaeologists have shown how important colours, shine, smells and other sensory properties of materials and artefacts were to societies in the past. Because of the impact they made on the senses and emotions, quite apart from the meanings that were ascribed to them, these characteristics played an essential role in the construction and transformation of their social organisation and life.

Colour was a fundamental issue in the past. The selection or production of materials in the different technologies was to a large extent guided by it: metalsmiths clearly set out to achieve particular colours with the alloys they used and the surface finishes they produced, for example. There was a tremendous diversity in the meanings that colours were attributed with, although some associations were recurring themes. Reddish tones were associated with blood, heat, transformation and female matters, greens with regeneration, flowering and vegetation, and whites and yellows with semen and the Sun. The countless different shades, designs and textures that are found in Colombian archaeological artefacts reveal a deep concern for colour. **MAU**

Necklace made of cornelian beads
187 CM
SIERRA NEVADA
DE SANTA MARTA,
TAIRONA PERIOD.
900 A.D. - 1600
A.D.
L03452

Necklace made of sub-globular gold and stone beads
32.5 X 0.8 CM
PALMIRA,
VALLE DEL CAUCA.
CALIMA REGION,
MALAGANA PERIOD.
200 B.C. - 200 A.D.
033641

Painted bowl
9.6 X 19.3 CM
NARIÑO HIGH
PLAINS,
LATE PERIOD.
600 A.D. -
1600 A.D.
C04858

Necklace made of
quartz beads
108 CM
PALMIRA,
VALLE DEL CAUCA.
CALIMA REGION,
MALAGANA PERIOD.
200 B.C. - 200 A.D.
L03402

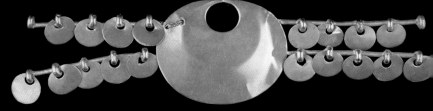

Nose ring with hanging plates
4.2 X 17.4 CM
MOÑITOS, CÓRDOBA
CARIBBEAN PLAINS, ZENÚ TRADITION
200 B.C. - 1600 A.D.
033469

The Magic of Things that Glitter

Shine was one of the sensory characteristics that boasted the greatest number of symbolic associations and special perceptions amongst pre-Hispanic societies. A profound sacred philosophy surrounded shine, and gave meaning to glossy cultural objects and to luminous phenomena in nature, leading to an aesthetic approach being adopted which favoured certain raw materials and finishes. Metalsmiths and potters and other crafters specially sought out materials that were shiny *per se* or were to some extent transparent, or which were known to be capable of acquiring and keeping a lustre, such as gold, quartz, jadeite and hard woods. At the same time, they developed numerous polishing and burnishing techniques, in order to obtain reflecting surfaces.

The Sun, the Moon, lightning and water, together with shiny artefacts, were associated by many societies with the supernatural forces that were responsible for life in the world. Mirrors and other archaeological objects made of obsidian, pyrite, quartz and metal were magical, prophetic instruments whose reflecting qualities, it was believed, meant they could communicate with supernatural beings and worlds or take part in their life-creating process. **MAU**

Pendant
8 X 7.5 CM
BARROSO, GUAMO, TOLIMA
MID-MAGDALENA VALLEY,
MIDDLE PERIOD
1 A.D. - 700 A.D.
O03231

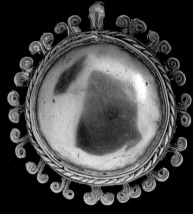

PLATES AND FLASHES OF LIGHT

One notable feature of virtually all
Colombian pre-Hispanic metalwork
is the importance that was given
to hanging plates. Many of these
objects were used in ceremonies at
night or in enclosed spaces where
the illumination - by torches or bonfires - was
poor. While people were dancing, the hanging
plates on ornaments must have filled the
surroundings with flashes of light and metallic
sounds, acting as a stimulus for states of
mind which favoured communication with
supernatural worlds. **MAU**

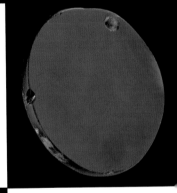

Obsidian mirror
6.6 X 3.2 CM
NARIÑO HIGH PLAINS,
LATE PERIOD.
600 A.D. - 1600 A.D.
L03425

**Earrings with
hanging plates**
7 X 16 CM, 8 X 14 CM
MID-CAUCA, LATE PERIOD.
700 A.D. - 1600 A.D.
O01727, O01728

Metaphors of the Cosmos

Metalworking societies projected their images of the cosmos in lakes or on hills, in their technologies and activities, and in the human body, houses and artefacts. Because of their profound symbolic associations, metals, and particularly gold, were favourite materials for expressing these images, on ornaments, containers and offering figures. These objects were depositaries for the world's cultural constructions, and reminded people of the prescribed forms of conduct.

The human body has been associated with representations of the universe in virtually all societies around the world. The body is often imagined as having been built in the image of the cosmos, and ornaments and paint are used on the basis of these associations. Colombian archaeological artefacts are notable for the rich face and body paint designs on the human figures, and these must have had cosmological meanings, in many cases. **MAU**

Anthropomorphous mask
with facial decoration
8.7 X 12.7 CM
RICAURTE, PÁEZ, CAUCA
TIERRADENTRO, MIDDLE PERIOD.
150 A.D. - 900 A.D.
O28918

Trumpet with geometric figures
40 X 5.6 CM
PALMIRA,
VALLE DEL CAUCA
CALIMA REGION,
MALAGANA PERIOD.
200 B.C. - 200 A.D.
O33395

Phytomorphous lime container
24.5 X 7.2 CM
TARAZÁ,
ANTIOQUIA
MID-CAUCA,
EARLY PERIOD.
500 B.C.
- 700 A.D.
O33160

The Home and the Temple, Mirrors of the Universe

Some societies in pre-Hispanic times, as they do even today, imagined their temples and their chieftains' enclosures to be identical, sacred replicas of the cosmos, situated in the navel or at the centre of the world. Their floors, divisions and roofs were identified with different levels or layers: the doors were thought to be the channels that linked those layers together, while the posts on which the roofs rested represented supports for the cosmos and the *axis mundi*. Inside, people behaved in accordance with this cosmological order: from there, priests and rulers recorded the movements of the stars so they could arrange collective activities and ceremonies. The cosmos could also be depicted as a big house, as the first, archetypal one, built at the very beginning of time.

The Muiscas on the high plains of Cundinamarca and Boyacá imagined that the enclosures surrounded by palisades, inside which were the houses of the chieftains, were a living organism, apparently the body of the chieftain himself. According to linguistic evidences, the door was believed to be his mouth, the central post his skeleton, and the ceremonial path his stomach. Besides, in votive metalwork figures which depict these enclosures, the chieftain's enormous body occupies the centre of the area. Blood from human and bird sacrifices - on the tops of the posts at the entrance to the palisade - was supposed to feed the enclosure - world - body. **M A U**

**Votive figure in the form
of an enclosure with
anthropomorphous figure**
12.6 X 6.1 CM
RADAMONTAL, COGUA,
CUNDINAMARCA
EASTERN CORDILLERA,
MUISCA - GUANE PERIOD
600 A.D. - 1600 A.D.
O08319

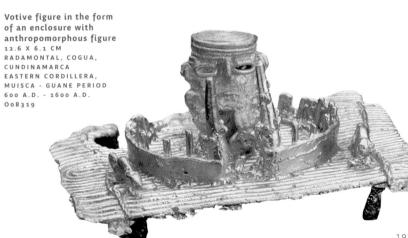

Votive figure in the form of an enclosure
with anthropomorphous figure
2.9 X 3.1 CM
RADAMONTAL, COGUA, CUNDINAMARCA.
EASTERN CORDILLERA, MUISCA - GUANE PERIOD.
600 A.D. - 1600 A.D.
O08454

Votive figure in the form
of an enclosure with
anthropomorphous figure
10.5 X 4.5 CM
SOGAMOSO, BOYACÁ.
EASTERN CORDILLERA,
MUISCA - GUANE PERIOD.
600 A.D. - 1600 A.D.
O05561

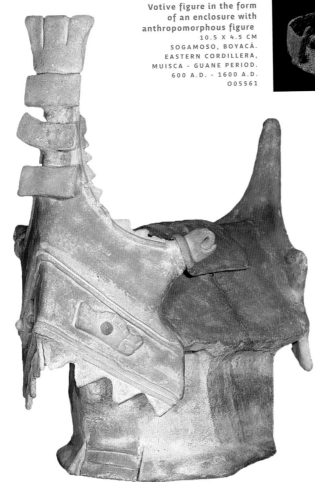

Offering
receptacle in
the form of a
house or temple
34 X 34 CM
EL ROSARIO,
TUMACO, NARIÑO.
PACIFIC COAST,
INGUAPÍ PERIOD.
700 B.C. - 350
A.D.
C13121

A Poporo *with a History*

Each object in the Museum has its own individual history, a history that dates back to very ancient times but which did not end when the object was buried in a grave or become lost in the mists of time. These artefacts underwent a number of profound changes while they were in the ground, and then, since they were unearthed, they have played a role - a very important one in some cases - in more recent events. The "Quimbaya *poporo*", or simply "the *poporo*", as it is frequently known, has a memorable history, one which began in Antioquia in the early years of the Christian era and which, since the 19th century, has been closely linked with that of Colombian archaeology in general and the Museum in particular.

According to the notes of geographer Agustín Codazzi, the *poporo* had already been discovered by 1850, in Pajarito, between Yarumal, Campamento and Angostura in north east Antioquia, as part of a rich funerary attire. A picture of it was published for the first time in 1885, in *Historia y Geografía de Antioquia* by Manuel Uribe Ángel, a key text for gaining an appreciation of the country's indigenous past and archaeological heritage. A photo of it also appeared around that time on the visiting cards of the Antioquia elite. Later, in 1939, Banco de la República acquired the *poporo*, to initiate the Gold Museum's metalwork collection. **M A U**

Phytomorphous lime container
23.5 X 11.4 CM
PAJARITO, ANGOSTURA, ANTIOQUIA.
MID-CAUCA, EARLY PERIOD.
500 B.C. - 700 A.D.
O00015

The Offering

Anthropomorphous pendant
6.6 X 4.9 CM   EL JAPÓN, SAN MARCOS, SUCRE
CARIBBEAN PLAINS, ZENÚ TRADITION
200 B.C. - 1600 A.D.
O25533

*M*ETAL THAT IS transformed by goldsmiths returns to its place of origin. It takes the form of the bird-shaman who flies through the middle, upper and lower worlds. It adopts the posture of the seated shaman who, in his hallucinatory trance, reveals the secrets of the cosmos and controls the forces that regulate life.

Metal objects return to the earth as gifts to the gods. Imbued with profound religious meanings, they are offered up in lakes and caves, in order to restore balance in the world. The metal cycle is thus completed; manipulated by man, it is used by him to manage the universe. MAU

Tobacco used to be people. It liked stories, and so when it heard voices in a house, it crept up to the wall and listened. That's why the Mother always made it grow around houses, near the wall. There it can listen. The Mother also ordered that tobacco should be taken with coca, because then it can hear all the stories.

KOGUI MITHOLOGY

GALLERY 4

Anthropomorphous votive
figure sitting in the
"basket" position
10.6 X 7 CM
EASTERN CORDILLERA,
MUISCA - GUANE PERIOD.
600 A.D. - 1600 A.D.
O00086

Male figure sitting
on a bench
22 X 8 CM
SAN FRANCISCO,
GUAITARILLA, NARIÑO.
NARIÑO HIGH PLAINS,
LATE PERIOD.
600 A.D. - 1600 A.D.
C04780

The Flight of the Shaman
Sitting down to Think

Thinkers in present-day indigenous societies, who have the task of guarding and passing on the oral tradition, adopt certain special body postures which are considered culturally appropriate for thinking. These postures are chosen for symbolic reasons, not just because they make it easier to concentrate. Two such postures can be clearly recognised in Colombian archaeological materials: one is where the person is sitting on a low bench or stool, the other where he is sitting on the floor, with legs bent and his arms around his knees. The first technique seems to have been more common in regions like Nariño, where it is frequently found in pottery, while the second was probably more popular on the high plains of Cundinamarca and Boyacá, judging by the numerous votive metalwork figures.

Among present-day indigenous societies both postures are imbued with rich symbolisms, ideas that probably date back to ancient times. The stool or bench is an essential part of the shaman's paraphernalia, and a symbol that is associated with wisdom, equilibrium and power. When the shaman sits on his bench, he feels transformed and that he is transported to the centre of the world, from where he travels along the *axis mundi* and enters deep into the spiritual dimension of reality. The "basket" position, as the other technique is called, because of the posture the body adopts, is intimately linked to the meaning of this particular artefact. The basket is a metaphor for, or image of, the person. People are viewed as being a basket that is continually woven with thought fibres, with the words that were uttered by the ancestors and the shaman; learning is therefore building, and filling the basket-body with knowledge about culture and tradition. MAU

Anthropomorphous votive figure sitting in the "basket" position
8 X 6 CM
EASTERN CORDILLERA,
MUISCA - GUANE PERIOD.
600 A.D. - 1600 A.D.
003044

Birds and Flight, Symbols of the Shaman

Birds are one of the most important themes in Colombian pre-Hispanic metalwork, one that is believed to be closely linked to shamanism. They are frequently seen in flight, with spread wings and tail, an iconography that various specialists have interpreted as alluding to the flight of the shaman. The majority are highly schematic figures, with only a few of the features depicted in detail. Those that can be recognised include eagles, falcons, sparrowhawks, condors and other birds of prey, along with parrots, macaws, toucans and hummingbirds.

There are many reasons why shamans were associated with birds. During their hallucinatory experience, which is the means they use most frequently to gain access to the supernatural world, it often feels as if the spirit were separating from the body, rising up and taking flight. Certain substances make the person feel as if he is viewing the earth from on high, or that he is closer to the stars. A Muisca priest from the village of Ubaque told the Spaniards that he went as far as Santa Marta in his flights and then got back to his village the same night. He made these trips under the effects of *yopo*, a strong hallucinogen that these priests specialised in. Birds were also viewed by many peoples as principal allies of the shaman and his most notable symbols, because of attributes like their mating dances, their migratory habits, the contribution they made to nature reproducing, their wisdom when hunting, and their brilliant colours. MAU

Breastplate in the form of a two-headed bird
11.7 X 11.2 CM
EL JAPÓN, SAN BENITO ABAD, SUCRE.
CARIBBEAN PLAINS, ZENÚ TRADITION.
200 B.C. - 1600 A.D.
O24108

Breastplate in the form of a bird.
13.6 X 11.7 CM
SAN PEDRO DE LA
SIERRA, CIÉNAGA,
MAGDALENA
SIERRA NEVADA
DE SANTA MARTA,
NAHUANGE PERIOD
200 A.D. - 900 A.D.
O16791

Pendant in the form of a bird.
8.4 X 6.7 CM
EL ROBLE,
GACHANCIPÁ,
CUNDINAMARCA
EASTERN CORDILLERA,
MUISCA - GUANE
PERIOD
600 A.D. - 1600 A.D.
O06783

Breastplate in the form of a bird-man with anthropomorphous and zoomorphous figures.
24 X 15.8 CM
PALETARÁ, PURACÉ, CAUCA.
UPPER CAUCA, LATE PERIOD.
900 A.D. - 1600 A.D.

A Majestic Bird-Shaman

One of the most outstanding bird-man images, a recurring transformation theme in the Museum's metalwork collection, is a Cauca-style breastplate, which is notable for its impressive appearance, iconographic complexity, and large size. The figure seemingly depicts a male shaman transformed into a bird of prey, perhaps an eagle or falcon, in view of its hooked beak and enormous spread tail.

A particularly prominent feature is the large, forked, feathered headdress, with its fine fretwork. This creates an effect of symmetry and equilibrium with the tail, and was perhaps a copy of a complex headdress that was worn by shamans in Upper Cauca during the Late Period. The legs and arms can be seen to be deformed through the use of ligatures, while grooves can be seen on the skin, like those on frog pendants from the same region. The hands and feet are also similar to the ones on these animal figures. Equally worthy of note are the four surrounding creatures, which are smaller, simplified versions of the figure himself and were probably his auxiliary beings. These were complemented by two quadruped-birds at the sides, fantastic creatures that would also have helped him in his flight and in his activities. MAU

Father Yoi thought, "Now my children are grown up, I'm going to throw the first party, so they can learn and follow my example". He taught us this, and ever since then it has been done. He did it in the time of darkness, with all his people, to cheer the world up right down to the present day. It can be heard with all the instruments: tortoise shells, drums, trumpets, and the noise of all the people. The crown the father was wearing was of feathers from the tail of the sparrow hawk. Everyone wore large earrings that shone, and they all painted their faces with juice from the huito plant.

TICUNA, AMAZONAS

Votive raft
10.2 X 10.1 CM
PASCA, CUNDINAMARCA.
EASTERN CORDILLERA,
MUISCA - GUANE PERIOD.
600 A.D. - 1600 A.D.
O11373

The Muisca Raft

Ever since the first European conquistadors set foot on American soil, the search for riches was the main motivation for their expeditions. One of the legends that grew up and became popular at the time was that of El Dorado, a distant land full of riches. As the Spaniards approached Muisca territory in 1537, they began to hear rumours of a ceremony where a great chieftain covered in gold dust threw large quantities of gold and emeralds to the bottom of a lake. Ever since then, the offering ceremony that the Muiscas held periodically on Guatavita lake, and possibly on others as well, has been associated with the El Dorado legend.

The Muiscas had, in fact, been making offerings for a very long time, not only at Guatavita but also at Siecha, Ubaque, Guasca, Teusacá, Iguaque and other lakes. These ceremonies, which people from distant parts flocked to, were governed by sowing and harvest times, and possibly also by the movements of the stars. The Spaniards misinterpreted the meaning of the offerings, and related them to a dynastic succession ceremony of the kind they were used to seeing in Europe. The main thing for them, however, was to confirm that the fabulous riches of the El Dorado legend could be on the beds of the lakes. An aggressive exploitation campaign thus began, and this lasted right into the Republican era. Guatavita lake was virtually destroyed, and others, such as Siecha and Fúquene, were seriously affected. The water level of Guatavita was reduced from what it had been in the 16th century, and the lake was completely dried out in 1911. The drainage channels were later blocked off and it was able to regain part of its volume. A deep tunnel was dug at Siecha, which reduced the level but caused a landslide and killed the

looters. Many offerings were recovered during these looting activities, many of them made of gold, but the famous El Dorado was never found.

The partial drying out of Siecha lake in the late 19th century resulted in a votive figure depicting an important person standing on a raft, surrounded by companions, being rescued. The coincidence between the iconography of this figure and the description of the Guatavita ceremony, as handed down by the 16th century Spanish chroniclers, led historians of the day to think that an image of the famous ritual had been found. Unfortunately, this first raft has not survived because, after passing to a collector, it was exported to Europe and on arrival at the port of Bremen, it was lost in a fire at a warehouse where it was awaiting collection.

It was therefore necessary to wait until 1969, when some hunters accidentally came across another raft, in a cave under a crag in the town of Pasca, south of Bogotá. This extraordinary object was found inside a large clay container decorated with a human figure with sharp teeth. In the same container were another gold figure, depicting a chieftain borne aloft on poles, and a simple pottery container. Thanks to the Pasca parish priest at the time, Father Jaime Hincapié, all these objects became part of the Gold Museum collection.

"The Muisca Raft", as it is popularly called, was made by casting using the lost wax method in a single operation, including the

ornaments and hanging plates of the different figures. It is made from a copper and gold alloy, but one where gold is the main element. It is 19.5 cm long, 10.1 cm wide, and 10.2 cm high. As far as what it depicts is concerned, the raft itself is a vessel apparently made from flexible trunks or some sort of reed, bent and tied at the ends to form a flat oval. The central figure, presumably a chieftain, is adorned with a headdress, earrings and nose ring; he is flanked by other, minor dignitaries, two of whom are carrying standards like those described by the chroniclers. RLL

Guatavita Lake

The Offering Ceremony

For the Muiscas of the Eastern Cordillera, the practice of making offerings was so widespread and so important that it can be said, without any fear of exaggerating, that every event in their social and individual life was an occasion for making an offering. Some of the Spanish chroniclers tell of how when someone was in need of something, he told his priest, and the priest then decided what should be offered up, and under what circumstances. The person took his offering, and the priest then sought a suitable occasion, usually in the early morning, to deposit it.

These accounts help us gain a better understanding of those involved in the offering act, and the circumstances surrounding it. Firstly, there needed to be a reason for making the offering - a special date such as the solstice or equinox, the start of sowing or harvesting, an event like a person's birth, puberty or death, a conflict, or a natural disaster. Those involved were, on the one hand, the people making the offering - a person, a family or a community - and an intermediary or religious official, who might have been the priest,

and on the other, the receiving party, a supernatural being, whoever the offering was being made to. The ritual established a specific place for the offering to be deposited, which might have been a lake, a cave or perhaps a field where crops were growing, and an occasion - a particular day, for astronomical reasons, or a precise time. Finally, the nature of the offering was of vital importance, since type and quantity changed in each case: a harvest offering at a solstice could not be the same as a funerary offering. All this meant that the act was a highly complex one, which required special knowledge.

There were also extraordinary offering ceremonies. People met from time to time by the moorland lakes to celebrate rituals like "running the land", when youngsters from many towns and villages took part in a race which took them via five sacred lakes, in each of which they deposited offerings. RLL

The Offering Room

The Exploratorium

The Gold Museum Exploratorium is somewhere different. Situated on the Museum's top floor, it has no archaeological objects on display. Rather, it sets out to make an impact on children and youngsters who begin their visit there, so as to change the way they view the archaeological galleries. Its themes stimulate an active visit, one where the visitor will explore each gallery, peep through cracks and have his curiosity roused, in order to discover a country that is full of diversity, understand how archaeologists decipher objects and contexts, or imagine what life must have been like for people who dug an enormous canal system 2000 years ago to control floodwater in the Zenú region. For people who arrive at the Exploratorium at the end of their tour, it is a place for reflection: can this ancient heritage that the Gold Museum is preserving help us think about ourselves, about who we Colombians really are? What can the lives of the indigenous societies who inhabited this same land in the past teach us about our own lives, about the society we are building together for the future? **EL**

In both the Museum and the Exploratorium, we want active visitors: children, youngsters and adults who are surprised by what they see, who enjoy their curiosity. We like those who ask themselves questions, observe, make comparisons with their previous experience and with what the expert has written, people who express opinions and draw their own conclusions. A museum is a place to explore things, but to explore ourselves at the same time. **EL**

Inside the Museum

The Gold Museum is a complex organisation, one where many people and branches, all of them specialists in different areas, work together. When artefacts first arrive at the Museum, they are received by a team of archaeologists, restorers and recorders. The archaeologists gather information about the context of the objects, checking all data that might be of use in their researches: where the objects were found, whether it was in a grave or somewhere else, for example. The restorers undertake an evaluation of the state the artefacts are in, so they can decide whether they require treatment or how this should be done. The recorders enter information in the Museum's files, and see that the objects are properly cared for and kept safe.

However, this is no more than the first step. The Museum's function is to study and interpret objects, and to display them in such a way that they can illustrate how those ancient inhabitants lived and thought. This is achieved by planning exhibitions around a particular archaeological theme, such as the funeral and burial customs of different indigenous groups. This work brings in the archaeologists once more, but now in the role of curators - that is, as planners of, and with a responsibility for, the content of the displays -, and also museographers, who have the task of designing the area where the exhibition will be held and deciding what equipment will be needed, where objects will be positioned, and other matters such as illumination and supporting items like photographs, illustrations and videos.

The exhibitions, in turn, give rise to new areas that need looking at. Complementary activities are required, for handling the different groups of visitors. The public services, dissemination and education offices accordingly arrange lectures, workshops and guided tours of the Museum, publish catalogues and leaflets, produce a website full of information that everyone can enjoy, and provide schoolchildren throughout the country with interactive exhibitions in the form of didactic cases. The website, management, security, maintenance, the café-restaurant, all of these combine to ensure that the work the Museum does with its collections reaches as many people as possible. RLL

Glossary

alcarraza   twin-spouted vessel with a handle forming a bridge between the two, used for holding liquids. A typical archaeological artefact found in southwestern Colombia.

bahareque   building system typical of certain parts of America, where the walls of houses are made using interwoven reeds and clay. Homes built this way are also given the same name.

captain   name given by the Spaniards during the Conquest to the heads or authorities of minor political units called *captaincies* which came under a chieftain.

chieftain   political authority of the Taino indians in the West Indies, but term commonly used by the Spaniards to refer to a person holding any type of political, economic, military or religious power amongst the indigenous peoples of America. Head of a chieftainship (see *chieftainship*).

chieftainship   society where differences of rank exist between members of the social group, and with some degree of political centralisation under the authority of a chieftain.

complex   group of decorative, technological or formal items which identify a particular period or era.

enclosure   housing zone and large ceremonial area surrounded by a double fence made of tree trunks, with a sacrifice post and a path that was used for processions. Muisca markets, offering ceremonies and many political and religious events were held there.

ethno-history   approach which combines the tools used in history and anthropology for studying the processes that went on immediately after the European invaders reached America.

genipap   tree belonging to the Rubiaceae family whose fruit, in the form of berries, contains a black dye that many indigenous peoples used for painting their bodies or objects that were in everyday use.

guadua   plant species belonging to the *Poacea* (formerly gramineous) family, whose strong, flexible reeds are highly suitable as a building material.

jadeite   shiny, greenish-coloured, translucent semi-precious stone.

material culture   constructions, implements and other artefacts which make up the tangible remains or material expression of past societies.

panning   washing river sand in wooden trays or bowls in order to extract gold.

poporo   container used for holding the lime that is needed when the roasted coca leaf is being chewed.

provincia   term employed by the Spanish conquistadors to refer to the indigenous townships they encountered. Little is known today about the *provincias*, although some researchers believe they could be chieftainships or political units identifying a particular territory. They could also correspond to a way of designating ethnic differences.

radiocarbon   dating method used for dating organic materials preserved on archaeological sites, such as remains of charred wood, fibres, and bone remains. Also known as Carbon 14.

reserve   institution dating back to the colonial era that was introduced under the period of Spanish rule, consisting of a territory set aside for a community of Amerindian origin, with collective ownership deeds, and governed by a special autonomous statute with its own cultural traditions and guidelines.

shaman   religious specialist who, in some of the world's indigenous societies, has the power to cure, communicate with the spirits, and influence the forces of the cosmos for the wellbeing of his community. Shamans wield great political power because of the various powers they are deemed to hold, which include visionary and prophesying abilities.

Spondylus   bivalve mollusc shell found on the coasts of Peru and Ecuador, which was traded extensively in pre-Hispanic times because of its ritual importance, probably due to its bright orange, red and purple colours. Sometimes also called *mullu*, an Inca word.

style   in general terms, refers to the typical manner or way of doing something. In archaeology, it refers to all the similarities that exist between objects which identify a specific period or human group or specific social groups. These similarities help identify chronological or cultural changes.

tradition technological or cultural patterns which persist through time and are identifiable from certain diagnostic or particular characteristics.

yagé (Banisteriopsis caapi) liana or climbing plant possessing hallucinatory properties that has been used for centuries by indigenous communities in the Amazon jungle, who call it the magic liana, or *ayahuasca*. Used in ceremonies of a religious-shamanistic nature, it has become somewhat notorious due to it also being used in urban contexts by groups of fans.

yopo (Anadenanthera colubrina) tree from the seeds of which a hallucinatory powder or snuff is prepared. This is inhaled by shamans during ritual ceremonies. **J S P**

Practical Information

Visit The Gold Museum!
Public entrance:
Tuesday to Saturday: 9:00 a.m. – 6:00 p.m.
Sundays and Holidays: 10:00 – 4:00 p.m.
Closed every Monday throughout the
year and certain public holidays.

Free Admission
For school groups, children under 12, and
adults over 60.

Public Transport
Use Transmilenio Las Aguas route and
alight at Museo del Oro station.

Services
A permanent exhibition in four thematic
galleries, a gallery for temporary
exhibitions, and an Exploratorium.
Guided thematic tours in
Spanish and English.
Audioguides can be rented in
Spanish, English and French.
Accessible by disabled persons.
Wheelchairs available.

Shop

Restaurant Cafeteria

Café

Reservations
for guided tours, workshops
or special events

Suggested Tours
In order to ensure that you enjoy a
memorable experience at the Gold
Museum, make the most of the time
you have available for your visit. If you
have a couple of hours, we suggest
you rent an audioguide or tour one
of the galleries with the thematic
tour that is on offer at the time.
Don't miss the Offering Gallery.
If you have half a day, explore the
four galleries that make up the
permanent exhibition. Relax for
a while in the café / or have lunch
in the café / restaurant.
Find even more on the Gold
Museum collections at
www.banrepcultural.org/museo-del-oro

The Gold Museum
Banco de la República
Carrera 6 15-88
Bogotá, Colombia
℃ (571) 343 2222
Fax (571) 284 7450
www.banrepcultural.org/museo-del-oro
wmuseo@banrep.gov.co

english version
Michael Sparrow

archaeological objects photos
Clark Manuel Rodríguez Bernal,
Rudolf Schrimpff, Juan Mayr

other photos
Aldo Brando
Marianne Cardale-Procalima
Yezid Campos
Departamento Técnico Industrial
del Banco de La República
Ana María Falchetti
Roberto Lleras
Pablo Obando
Gerardo Reichel Dolmatoff
BLAA LIBRARY
Ana María Rivera
Juanita Sáenz
Diego Samper
Sebastián Schrimpff
Alberto Sierra
Fernando Urbina
Arturo Vargas

edited by
Eduardo Londoño Laverde
Sandra Patricia Mendoza Vargas

ilustrations / maps
Juan Manuel Ramírez
Javier Gutiérrez
Marco Robayo
The Silhouette

printing process supervision
Departamento de Documentación
y Editorial del Banco de la República

prepress / layout / printer
Javier Tibocha / Camilo Umaña / Nomos Impresores